3/19
5/18
3/20
rolreland.

£4
£1

THE *Wild* BOGLANDS

Pl. 1 Home sweet home. . . This is the last year that the curlew will be able to raise a family on this section of blanket bog. The eggs are safe in a nest of the leaves of bog rush and moor grass, and the chicks will have fledged and flown long before the bog, which has already been drained, is cut away. The habitat for one living thing will soon heat and light the home of another.

Pl. 2 Bogwebs. . . Spiders are among the commonest and most abundant dwellers of the bogland. Early morning is the best time to see their silken death traps string like tents over the vegetation. Insects emerging from beneath or dropping in from above will not escape.

Pl. 3 Get up and grow. . . A hummock in embryo, part of a raised bog in the making. Red bog moss, a hummock-former, is beginning to overgrow the yellow recurved bog moss which forms carpets around the hollows. Papillose, burgundy red, red and brown bog mosses are the main get-up-and-grow hummock-formers, while the feathery bog moss soon fills the hollows with a treacherous carpet.

Pl. 4 All-American immigrant. . . The pitcher plant was introduced into Ireland from America in 1909 and found certain bogs of the central plain very much to its liking. Insects which crawl into the open pitcher plant find it impossible to escape. They eventually drown in a watery grave, for the pitchers soon fill up with rain. The remains of the many insects which drown in this way help to provide the plant with nutrients, especially nitrogen.

2

2

CAITRÍONA DOUGLAS

3

CAITRÍONA DOUGLAS

6

7

Pl. 5 Daphnia and cyclops, alive alive oh. . . Daphnia the water flea complete with brood sac full of eggs and two cyclops, each, as their name suggests, with a single eye. Both are members of the Crustacea group, which also includes the crabs and lobsters. They feed on bacteria and smaller plants and animals and in turn they feed the bladderworts.

Pl. 6 Damsel in distress. . . A blue damsel fly has dropped in to a sticky end, trapped by the round-leaved sundew. Or has it the strength to escape? This is just one of no less than eleven spieces of carnivorous plants which thrive on the bogs of Ireland. Acid bogs are very poor in available nutrients, especially nitrogen, so what better way to overcome the problem than by digesting the odd insect or two.

Pl. 7 Bladderworts do it under water. . . A leaf of a bladderwort modified to form an underwater trap. The bladder is empty, the trap is set. Any small animal bumping against the trigger hairs is in for a shock. It will be whooshed into a semi-transparent prison, which will one day become its grave. Perhaps it is only fair that some plants should eat animals, for a change.

HEATHER ANGEL

HEATHER ANGEL

Pl. 8 Mountain hares. . . In the absence of the brown hare in Ireland, the mountain hare is found even on the lowland bogs, where it grazes the ling and cotton-grass. They are great runners, each making use of about twenty hectares of bog.

Pl. 9 . . . on form in the wetlands. As the largest blanket bog hummocks dry and die, they may become invaded by the aptly named lambswool moss. This one has made an ideal resting place for the hare, its form sunk in the soft moss is protected from the prevailing wind.

8

RICHARD MILLS

9

CAITRÍONA DOUGLAS

6

THE *Wild* BOGLANDS

BELLAMY'S IRELAND

Dr DAVID BELLAMY

Facts On File Publications
New York, New York ● Oxford, England

The publishers acknowledge the permission of Allen Figgis to reproduce extracts
from *The Way that I Went* by Robert Lloyd Praeger.

The publishers would like to express their thanks
for help and encouragement
during the preparation of this book to the following:

David Green; Rosemary Bellamy; Dr Jim Ryan and Dr John Cross of the Forest and Wildlife Service;
Dr Michael Ryan, Keeper of Irish Antiquities; Dr John Feehan;
Dr Peter Woodman, UCC; Helen Feighan, researcher;
Raghnall Ó Floinn; Éamon de Buitléar; Bord Fáilte; Bord na Móna; Dr Gerry Doyle;
Siobhán Parkinson; and all the photographers
who were so helpful in providing photographs.

First published in Ireland
by Country House Dublin

© 1986 Dr. David Bellamy.
First published in the United States in 1987
by Facts On File, Inc.

British Library Cataloguing in Publication Data

ISBN 0-8160-1746-8.

Managing Editor — Treasa Coady
Text Editor — Siobhán Parkinson
Designer — Bill Murphy
Typeset by Printset & Design Ltd., Dublin
Colour Reproduction by Kulor Centre
Printed and bound in Ireland.

Contents

		Page
INTRODUCTION		11
CHAPTER 1	PEAT GROWING WILD	17
CHAPTER 2	HOW TO RAISE A BOG	39
CHAPTER 3	THE WET BLANKET	57
CHAPTER 4	SALTS OF THE EARTH	79
CHAPTER 5	TAKING DOWN THE EVIDENCE	87
CHAPTER 6	EVIDENCE FROM UNDER THE BLANKET	95
CHAPTER 7	THE TALE OF THE LITTLE RED BOG	121
CHAPTER 8	WHAT CAN YOU DO WITH A BOG?	129
CHAPTER 9	CUT AND THRUST — PROSPECTS FOR THE FUTURE	151
APPENDIX 1	PLANTS AND PEAT TYPES	161
APPENDIX 2	BOGS FOR CONSERVATION	163
BIBLIOGRAPHY		167
INDEX		169

INTRODUCTION

Great Bog of Allen swallow down
That heap of muck called Philipstoun
And if thy mor can swallow more
Then take and relish Tullamore

J. SWIFT

The Boora complex of peatlands which stretched from the Shannon estuary almost to Dublin is no more. The Great Bog of Allen has itself been swallowed up by the gourmands of Philipstown, Tullamore and the Irish economy in their need for electricity. The signs of Bord na Móna, its great machines, electricity sub-stations and grid lines dominate the dead brown scene once dominated by the living cupolas of the great red bogs of the central Irish plain.

I was first introduced to those bogs by reading the books of Robert Lloyd Praeger, botanist, natural historian, historian and author of such note that I hardly dare follow in his footsteps. Yet follow I must, for if something isn't done, and quickly, a unique part of the world's living heritage could be lost for ever.

First, three short stories, vignettes of the Irish bogs as I remember them when as a student twenty-five years ago I came to know and understand their unique place within the created order of life upon this earth.

* * *

It was a fine morning with the promise of a good drying day. The location east of the Shannon estuary, exactly where is now of little matter, for back in those days there were many such bogs from which to choose.

Leaving the road, my wife Rosemary and I made our way across the hem of cutaway, peat banks criss-crossing deep dark pools, the surface of which floated rich embroideries of moss. The banks were hung with gossamer, the work of myriad spiders, each strand threaded with dew drops fresh distilled from the night air now alive in the sun. A frog splashed

11

in at our approach, rocking the delicate wax-yellow flowers of the bladderworts and launching a newly emerged damsel fly off into a new existence. If only we had wings!

Skirting the last open pool, we reached the working face, six feet or more; its top of fresh cut peat, though drying in the sun, still bore the shadows of its past, layers and lenses of varied textures, shades and substance. At the base, grey sticky clay could just be seen, a watertight seal laid across the landscape by glaciers which melted making way for plants, animals and people to come and make a living from this green and bounteous land. Above the clay the unmistakable remains of the common reed and above that a wedge of pure white peat made up of lambswool moss and lichen, all perfectly preserved exactly as they first grew upon this spot. We knew even then that we were looking at a gigantic slice of history, but only later did we come to understand the full significance of that find.

Our work for the day was to gather data concerning the flora of the bog, data that would eventually form part of my thesis and my life's work. We moved on up onto the bog as the sun climbed in the sky, a wind from the west kept us cool, and helped curlew and snipe up onto the wing.

The end result of our day's work would be a series of lists of plants with estimates of their importance in the living communities which turn sunlight and carbon dioxide into peat. A vast store of energy and information all laid down by plants which can survive in the most acid conditions and thrive on the meagre supplies of minerals brought in by those westerly winds.

Boring lists of Latin names, but at least we can now look at those lists and restructure in our minds the breathing surface of that living bog. Swelling hummocks of bog moss, brown, deep red, ochre, pink, appliquéd with the flowers of cranberry and crowned with cross-leaved heath and ling. Separating the hummocks are damper lawns of green, orange and gold punctuated by tufts of bog cotton and asphodel. The insect traps of the sundews crowd around pools which are almost choked with the yellow of feathery bog moss. They stand in wait for insects emerging from the pool. They hope to fly to freedom, their loss the sundew's gain.

Boring Latin names — no! Each one a part of a living, breathing, rising, falling community of plants and animals which live in the soft assurance that their remains will not decay but will stay as an epitaph, locked safe in the peaty record book. Ghosts of tomorrow's past, hidden power and an omen for our futures.

We walked and listened and walked some more until we were lost in the enormousness of the bogland scene, the roof of a peatland world, the surface of the bog sloping down in all directions to be lost as we were in the shimmer of a perfect summer's day.

It was late afternoon before we found ourselves once more back at the cutaway. There a picture book family, complete with donkey, creels and slains, were completing their day's hard work. We shared our bogland knowledge and experience and then were allowed to drink the essence of it all, not Tullamore Dew, but a fiery nectar befitting the wild wonder of the place in which we stood.

* * *

The year before, we had spent our honeymoon where else but amongst the bogs of Ireland. It was January 1959, and the frost jewelled both the callow and the bogs from the Lakes of Killarney where we stayed, clear up to Tullamore and beyond. The surface of each bog was frozen stiff like the crust of new baked bread and it seemed sacrilege to break such perfection. We waited till the warmth of a duck-egg-blue day had melted the rime. Then across the steaming bog we saw a sight of immense beauty and rarity. Skein upon skein of Greenland white-fronted geese rose up from the bog where they had spent the night in safety and made their way down to the callow to graze.

The bogs of Ireland are now the only winter home for more than sixty per cent of all that is left of the world population of this rare goose. If the bogs are all cut away, where will they go? to extinction?

* * *

A not so fine spring day and a car ride west out of Dublin with Father John J. Moore, Professor of Botany at University College Dublin. The journey took us across the Curragh where John explained as only he could the way these acid heathy lands had come into being.

Stripped of their trees in stone age times, their freely draining soils were opened up to the leaching power of the rain now falling about our ears. The early farmers moved on and the acid loving heath plants moved in to provide Ireland with the perfect proving ground for some of the best bloodstock in the world. I will always remember the excitement in John's

13

voice as he told the story of those first farmers and those who followed bringing Christianity to these shores and carving great stone crosses to show the strength of their faith.

We followed those leached minerals down to where they still fed an area of callow rich in reeds and black bog rush and there he opened my mind to the true wonders of creative evolution as seen through the eyes of a man of God and science.

* * *

God's first commandment to people was to have dominion over all the living things upon this earth, and that includes the bogs of Ireland. That is why I had to write this book.

I do not dedicate it to Robert Lloyd Praeger, nor to John J. Moore. They have their dedication in all the knowledge they gained and imparted. No, I dedicate it to the board, the officers and the workforce of Bord Na Móna. With real respect for all they have done in the past to develop the peatland resource, for what they are doing to supply Ireland with the electricity it needs and what they must now do to ensure that the uniqueness of Ireland's peatland heritage does not disappear.

The people of Ireland inherited this richness from the past, please don't steal it all from future generations.

ACKNOWLEDGEMENTS

To Treasa Coady who made this book possible. To Robert Lloyd Praeger for many hours of fascinating reading. To Father John J. Moore for leading me through the paths of knowledge. To Jim Ryan and John Cross for correcting and updating my scientific facts. To Siobhán Parkinson for taking a manuscript written while in orbit with many other things and restructuring it into a readable whole. Any credit is theirs, any mistakes are mine. Finally to Meriel Steel for reading my appalling writing and typing the first draft.

DAVID BELLAMY
Bedburn 1986

CHAPTER 1:
PEAT GROWING WILD

What is Peat?

The scientific definition of peat is partially decayed organic matter mainly of plant origin. In everyday language, peat — or turf as it is called in Ireland — is made up of the partly rotted remains of roots, stems, leaves, flowers, fruits, seeds and even tiny pollen grains and spores. In theory, any plant community can form peat, given the right conditions; in practice, however, few do so, because most plants cannot grow and thrive under those conditions, the most important of which is that the soil and the peat that forms on it are saturated with water for much or all of the year.

Anybody with a compost heap in their garden is in fact in the peat-producing business. They will know that a well-regulated heap, not too dry and not too wet or too cold, soon turns perfectly recognisable plant remains into thick, brown-black, almost uniform humus, perfect for digging back into the garden. They will also know that if the heap is not well regulated and fed with 'accelerator' minerals, then the whole thing can stagnate, rotting down will be incomplete and the resulting humus will be sour, smelly and full of partly decomposed twiggy bits and tough leaves, easy to identify but not much good for the cabbage patch. They will know too that little or nothing will grow on or in the close environs of the working compost heap and that even the pools of humus-stained water which leak from it are no-grow areas except for a few highly tolerant weeds.

A bog is in fact a giant inefficient compost heap, which, left to its own devices, can never complete its rotting process because it is super-saturated with water. It is a gigantic store of energy and chemicals that can be an investment for all our futures and a repository of information relating to all our pasts.

Life in Watery Conditions

We all know that without water there would be no life on earth; but too much water in the wrong place can slow down the pace of life and even kill, and this is especially true for creatures like us which are *aerobic* (which depend on oxygen).

Unfortunately, oxygen is not very soluble in water. Any aquarium owner will understand the importance of having a bubbler or oxygenating plants, because without some method of putting oxygen back into the water even the hardiest goldfish cannot survive.

Any body of water — even a goldfish bowl — is home to many microscopic aerobic organisms, bacteria, fungi, protista (minute animals) and the like, which get their energy by consuming other living things and their remains. In so doing they rapidly use up any oxygen that is present in the water. In a mountain stream or river this is not too much of a problem as oxygen is constantly being stirred into water that tumbles over rocks and waterfalls. Even in a large lake, the wind will stir the surface helping oxygen to dissolve and many microscopic plants — the phytoplankton — will oxygenate the surface layers. Under such conditions, if something dies its remains will rapidly be attacked by a whole host of what are best called *decomposer organisms*, nature's own refuse disposal operatives, which use up the energy contained in the carcasses and other waste, returning the minerals back into the water to feed the whole process once more. This is how the normal natural cycle of life and death goes round and round and keeps going round and round year after year.

However, even in a well-regulated lake, the vital work of the decomposer organisms can use up the store of oxygen so that fish and other larger aerobic creatures begin to die and their remains start to accumulate. If this can happen in an open lake, imagine the problems of a waterlogged soil. A waterlogged soil has none of the advantages of an open body of water and all the disadvantages. The soil water is stagnant, or at the best very slow-moving, and so oxygen will not be stirred in. Also, light cannot penetrate far between the solid particles, so any photosynthetic activity will take place only in the surface layers; deeper down any oxygen present will soon be used up.

So acute is this problem that the majority of plants which grow in aquatic and waterlogged conditions have one structural feature in common: their bulk is made up of an open meshwork of living cells separated by a complex of air spaces. This special tissue is called *aerenchyma*. Under the microscope it looks very beautiful and is very reminiscent of the geodesic design of the air frame of a modern aeroplane; in fact it almost looks as if one has copied the other. The geodesic design was the idea of the famous inventor, Barnes Wallace, and was used to give maximum strength with minimum weight to both air ships and air planes. Aerenchyma is the result of millions of years of creative evolution, its function to give maximum strength with minimum use of cells, all of which will require a supply of oxygen to keep them alive and healthy — ideal for a plant growing in an environment subject to oxygen stress. Added advantages of this special tissue are lightness and buoyancy, which means it can float — ideal in a watery habitat — and a system of air spaces that can store and transport oxygen around the plant and beyond.

18

Study of a number of such plants has shown that they can enrich the soil and peat around their roots with oxygen, presumably transported down via their aerenchyma, producing an upper layer in the peaty soil which is richer in oxygen. In dry periods, when the water table is not right up to the surface, oxygen-rich air can diffuse down amongst the soil and peat particles. So it is that many aerobic decomposer organisms can thrive in the upper layers, and here decomposition will take place more rapidly at certain times of the year, using up any oxygen that is present.

The Anaerobic Zone

Below this *semiaquatic* (head just above water) layer in which most of the living roots are situated there is an *anaerobic* zone, a no-grow area for aerobic life. You can prove the existence of the anaerobic layer either in a bog or in your badly regulated compost heap in a very simple but graphic way. Take a long stiff copper wire and clean it thoroughly until it shines in the sun. Then insert it into the peat bog or compost heap and leave it untouched for several days. On removing the wire you will find that the lower end is stained black with a deposit of copper sulphide. You can do a similar, more up-market experiment using a long silver spoon, when the black deposit will be silver sulphide.

The sulphide is a by-product of the life processes of some very special bacteria which can thrive only in the total absence of free oxygen. They too are decomposer organisms obtaining their energy from sugars and other organic compounds, the remains of plants and animals, and their oxygen from sulphates dissolved in water. Probably the commonest sulphate present is dilute sulphuric acid (H_2SO_4) (H_2 = two hydrogen atoms; S = one sulphur atom; O_4 = four oxygen atoms). The oxygen is used up by the bacteria and the sulphur is voided into the environment, ending up either as copper or silver sulphide (CuS or AgS), which colours the wire or the spoon black, or as hydrogen sulphide (H_2S) which makes the peat smell of bad eggs or sixth-form chemistry lessons.

Two other products of this anaerobic decomposition are methane or marsh gas, CH_4 (C = one carbon atom; H_4 = four hydrogen atoms), which is the main constituent of natural gas and is of course highly flammable, and phosphine, PH_3 (one phosphorus and three hydrogen). The latter is so flammable that it spontaneously ignites on exposure to the oxygen in the air to produce the dancing will-o'-the-wisps which help to make bogs such mysterious places.

All these are products of the dank, dark world of the anaerobic layer, a glimpse of what life was like on earth some three billion years ago, long before there were any green, photosynthetic plants to produce free oxygen. Back in those far-off days the abundance of life was less and the pace of life much slower. The pace of decomposition in a waterlogged soil is also very slow, and in the depths of the anaerobic layer, to which even the warming rays of the sun never reach, it is almost nil. That is why peat — or partly decomposed plant remains — accumulates.

Problems of Life on the Surface of the Peat

As the peat layer grows it seals off any contact with the mineral soil from which all the mineral nutrients for plant and animal growth were originally derived.

The plants growing on the surface of the peat soon become totally dependent on the meagre supplies of minerals brought in by the rain and wind. So it is little wonder that many plants with novel ways of supplementing their mineral intake are found on the peatlands, and none more novel than the plants which trap and digest insects and other creepy crawlies. No less than eleven species of carnivorous plants occur on the Irish peatlands and they include sundews, butterworts, bladderworts and a pitcher plant.

The pitcher plant, though introduced only in 1906 from its native North America, soon became very much at home on the Irish scene and can be seen growing on a number of bogs on the central plain. It is a passive trapper: insects falling, flying or crawling into the funnel of the pitcher-shaped leaves find it very difficult to get out and eventually perish in a watery grave. The top flap of the trap does not close, indeed once open its only function is as a rather ineffective umbrella which helps to stop the pitcher filling with rain too quickly.

The sundews and butterworts are also passive trappers, both working on the principle of the fly paper. Glands on the highly modified leaves produce a sweet stickum which both attracts and traps the hapless prey. A well-grown plant of the long-leaved sundew can easily trap and hold a large dragonfly, the most fabulous of Irish insects, which is not uncommon around bogland pools.

For a long time it was thought that these plants were active trappers, the long glandular hairs of the sundews moving to help hold their prey and the margin of the butterwort leaf rolling to do the same. You may of course sit and watch one of these strange plants at work and try to decide for youself. Do those long hairs of the sundew really move of their own accord or is it the death struggles of the insect that draw them together in a sinister curve towards the prey? The leaf of the butterwort unrolls in its normal course of development, exposing the butter-yellow adhesive surface. Any insect caught by its glue will try to escape, and many crawl towards and underneath that rolled margin, the end result being to make the leaf appear more aggressive than it really is. But no, both are passive trappers. Or are they? Take a look for yourself.

It was Charles Darwin, no less, who first showed that when starved of insects such plants did not grow as well as those that were regularly fed. Study using the powers of scanning electron microscopes and other modern scientific instruments and methods has proved that the leaves and traps are well furnished with short glandular hairs which secrete a number of very special chemicals called digestive enzymes. It has also been proved that these help to digest the carcass of the insect prey, and that the products of digestion, especially potassium (K), nitrogen (N) and phosphorous (P) (those same chemicals which you put onto your kitchen garden as fertiliser), end up inside the predatory plant, helping to make it grow more strongly.

The bladderworts, which are active trappers, are perhaps the strangest of all, and on a world scale are certainly the most successful of all the carnivorous plants, there being at least two hundred different species, found mainly in the tropics. Ireland provides a warm, wet home for no less than four species, all of which thrive in its unpolluted waters. They catch their prey by means of underwater leaves, which are highly modified to form tiny bag-like traps. The mouth of each transparent trap is closed by a hinged door, itself well supplied with special hairs that are sensitive to touch and trigger the door. The trap, being made up of living cells, will fill with water by the process of osmosis and diffusion.

A living cell is in effect a concentration of chemicals including salts and sugars, surrounded by a special membrane which selectively keeps the chemicals in and the water out. If it was surrounded by a completely water-tight envelope, it would soon die because nothing could get in or out. Likewise, if it couldn't control water uptake and loss the cell would either lose all its life chemicals or it would become overfilled with water and burst. The process of control is called *osmosis*.

The bladderworts have the special ability to pump all the water out of their traps; no mean feat when you realise that a large plant may have many hundred traps. This is an active process using energy and so a constant drain on the resources of the plant. Once the trap is set, any insect or crustacean (such as a water flea, or a water shrimp) which brushes against the trigger hairs is in for a surprise. The door flies open and the prey is whooshed in with the inrush of water that refills the trap. This method of trapping poses a real problem when it comes to digestion of the prey, and the same is true in the case of the pitcher plant whose traps are also full of water. Any digestive enzymes which are secreted into the trap will be diluted by the water, and as the manufacture and secretion of such chemicals uses considerable amounts of energy, it could be a very wasteful process. So it would seem that in many cases the prey is not immediately killed and digested; in fact, it may go on living imprisoned in the trap — a life sentence. The faeces and finally the remains of the prisoner pass on to enrich the life of its gaoler-executioner or its murderer. Rough justice indeed!

All one can say in their defence is that the carnivorous plants at least in a very small way get their own back on the animal kingdom, the members of which usually sit high up on the food chain, totally dependent upon plants for all their needs, including their minerals.

So it is that eleven of Ireland's plants have overcome one of the main limitations of life on the surface of the peat. What of the rest?

The Recyclers

The major adaptation of plant life in the peatland environment is an ability not only to grab hold of any nutrients that are available but then to keep hold and recycle them from year to year. Recycling is greatly aided by the fact that the vast bulk of decomposition of plant and animal remains that does occur takes place in the upper peat layers, above the anaerobic zone, and that is exactly where the feeding roots of the plants are concentrated. However, minerals released by decay could be washed away and so it would appear that the plants have to maintain an even tighter hold, in effect a closed circuit.

It is now also known that many of the plants which dominate the peatland scene, like the bog cotton, are able, at the onset of autumn, to withdraw key minerals which are in short supply from their dying tissues and transport them down into the safety of their perennial parts. The wine-red tips of the bog cotton leaves and the orange tips of the scimitar-like leaves of bog asphodel and all the other autumn tints of the peatland surface let us know not only that the chlorophyll (green colouring) is being broken down, allowing the other colours to show through, but that those tissues are being emptied of useful minerals. Studies using radioactive tracers have shown that the minerals are stored down in the underground rhizomes, to be recycled up into the new growth of the following year. It is therefore little wonder that sheep and native herbivores like hares and grouse and geese, which graze on the bog vegetation, avidly seek out these young mineral-rich shoots as a key part of their diet in the spring. Likewise, during the winter the rare Greenland white-fronted geese grub up the nutrient-rich underground parts of bog cotton and white-beaked sedge.

For a long time, farmers who grazed their animals on peatland blamed the bog asphodel (*Narthecium ossifragum*, meaning fragile bones), whose yellow flowers are so dominant in the summer grazings, for the occurrence of rickets in their stock. Scientists pooh-poohed the idea, pointing out that it was the general lack of minerals and especially of calcium in the habitat and hence in their diet which caused the weakening of their bones. However, the farmers were right, for recent study has indicated that bog asphodel may contain an ingredient which antagonises the action of vitamin D, lack of which is the root — or in this case the shoot — cause of rickets.

Study has also shown that at normal levels of stocking and exploitation, sheep can be grazed on even the poorest types of peatland without adversely affecting either the sheep or the mineral balance of the system. In fact, the losses of key minerals due to the exploitation of the sheep for their wool or meat have been shown to be insignificant in proportion to other natural losses and are amply made up for many-fold by input from the rain. However, in cases where farmers have attempted to take a crop of plants from the bog to use as fodder for animals kept in other areas, nutrient loss has been so great as to curtail the regrowth of the plants. It is thus fair to compare the vegetation of peat bogs with that of tropical rain forests, for in both systems it is a fact that the vast bulk of the available nutrients are at all times in cycle in the living plant community, and little or nothing is in store in the soil. Removal of the standing crop of plants in either will lead to a breakdown of the system, and it will take many years for the nutrient store to be built up once again, so that the natural vegetation can grow again.

The farmers of Ireland have long known that it is impossible to cultivate their bogland without massive preparation and inputs of fertilisers. The developers are now learning this fact of life in areas of tropical rain forest. Destruction of these forests, which are one of the richest habitats for plants and animals on earth, results not in productive farms, but in semi-deserts of little use to people or nature.

The Xeromorphs

Another, much stranger, feature that bogs and tropical rain forests have in common is that the vast majority of their constituent plants are *xeromorphic*. This means that, like cacti and other semi-desert plants, they don't lose too much water when they are put under stress. This is a strange feature in plants that live in habitats which are well supplied with rain for the bulk of the year.

The problem in the rain forest is that when it is not actually raining, the hot tropical sun causes rapid and excessive evaporation, putting the plants, even the great trees, under water stress. If they could not effectively control the loss of water from their leaves, the living cells would be damaged and the plants could die. The same is also true for plants growing on exposed bogs in the height of a dry summer. There is also the added problem that in winter, when the bog surface is frozen, the plants will be unable to take up water through their roots. If they couldn't control water loss from their shoots, which are exposed to the desiccating (drying) winds of winter, they would soon be killed.

So it is that we find plants like ling and other members of the heather flower family with tiny, almost scale-like leaves growing on bogs: having small leaves reduces the amount of water loss. What is more, the leaves are often covered with a thick waxy protective cuticle and well supplied with an extra covering of long hairs over furrows or pits, in the bottom of which the *stomata* are situated. Stomata are the special pores through which the plant takes in the carbon dioxide necessary for photosynthesis and while the pores are open precious water vapour will escape.

Many of the sedges and rushes have needle-like leaves, which reduce the surface area from which water can evaporate; while plants like the cranberry and the bog pimpernel maintain a low profile, creeping across and flattening their leaves onto the humid surface of the living peat.

Perhaps the strangest adaptations of all are found in the bog mosses or *Sphagnum* mosses which, as we shall see, rank amongst the major peat formers of the world.

Although they are by definition aquatic mosses, each one is structured like a sponge to soak up and store water. Like most mosses, their leaves are made up of a single layer of cells; however, a look under the microscope or even a strong hand lens will reveal a network of two types of cell. The main bulk of each leaf is made of large dead empty cells, the walls of which are held apart by spiral bands of strengthening and are pierced by large pores to let the water in. Sandwiched between the large cells are elongate narrow cells which contain both living cytoplasm and an abundance of chloroplasts. These cells are the seat of the process of photosynthesis which allows the bog mosses to grow, carrying their own in-built reservoir ever upwards, engulfing anything which can't keep pace, relegating both it and its own remains down to the anaerobic zone.

Here perhaps is the real reason for all these water-conserving adaptations. The peat is in effect a gigantic reservoir of water, but its surface is unprotected from the weather by large plants, bushes and trees, and is hence subject to the full effects of all climatic fluctuations; so it becomes very hot and dries out rapidly in the summer, and freezes solid in the winter. All the plants, even the bog mosses themselves, must have the ability to store and conserve water as and when the need arises.

The structure of the bog mosses is also very special in another way, for it has been shown that, as they grow, not only do they produce the large dead and narrow living cells which are their hallmark of success, but, as an integral part of that structure, they produce complex chemical compounds called (sorry about the long words) *unesterified polyuronic acids*. These compounds, which impregnate the cell walls, have the very useful property of being able to exchange hydrogen ions, which are a by-product of their life processes, for minerals such as calcium, magnesium, potassium and the like, present in the water. This is very useful in a plant that grows in a mineral-deficient habitat. Thus, as they grow, they swap one of their main waste products, hydrogen ions, for the minerals they need for growth — calcium, important in the structure of cell walls, magnesium, a key component of chlorophyll, and sodium and potassium, key ingredients of the living process. So it is that the bog mosses can grab any minerals which come their way.

An Acid Environment

This system of swapping hydrogen ions for necessary minerals works very well for the bog mosses, but there is another side to the story. The hydrogen ions so released acidify the water, and thus the whole peatland environment, unless there are bases (such as bicarbonate) present in the waters to keep them neutral.

Any good farmer or gardener knows that if the soil becomes too acid many plants will become stunted and may die. To counteract this effect, he or she will add lime (calcium hydroxide, $Ca(OH)_2$ — two calcium atoms and two hydroxyl ions) to the soil. It is the hydroxyl part which helps to put the soil back into good growing fettle. If the numbers of hydrogen ions (H^+) and hydroxyl ions (OH^-) balance out in the soil water it will be neutral. If there are excess hydrogen ions present, the water becomes acid or sour, and if there are excess hydroxyl ions it becomes alkaline or caustic. Too much of either is bad for most forms of life, so the delicate living cells will do their level best to keep themselves around the point of neutrality, because if the balance is tipped too far either way they will die.

So important is this acid–alkali balance that we have all sorts of sophisticated gadgets to allow us to measure it and a special scale with which to express it. The scale is called the pH scale, and it runs from pH1 to pH14. pH7 is the point of neutrality when acids and bases exactly balance out, anything below pH7 is acid in reaction, anything above pH7 is alkaline, and as far as life is concerned the further from neutrality the greater the problem.

Once the bog mosses have got a firm foothold, the problems of acidity will be added to those of the peatland surface. Life on the surface of the bog isn't all sweetness; in fact it is exactly the opposite. Too much water and too little oxygen round your roots, not enough shade around your shoots, too few minerals and galloping acidity — it's a wonder that any plants survive, but survive they do, in fact they thrive.

Peat-Forming Plants and Peat Types

When it comes to discovering which plants are best adapted to the harsh conditions of bogland life, the student has one great advantage. An inefficient compost heap not only stores energy and chemicals, it also stores information in the identifiable shape and form of stems, twigs, leaves, roots, rhizomes, fruits, seeds, spores and pollen grains. They are not fossils in the true sense of the word for they have not been impregnated with mineral material. Despite this, and in part because of it, many of the features of these subfossils are perfectly preserved and so they may be identified by experts.

A peat bog is thus a giant history book which chronicles its own development in a very intimate and intricate way. To ascertain which plants can tolerate the rigours of life as a peat producer, all you have to do is to study the plant remains found in the peat. The only problem is that it takes great patience, skill and knowledge. The first scientist to make a comprehensive and formalised study of this aspect of peatlands was a Polish botanist by the name of Stanislaus Tolpa. His work showed that the many different types of peat, all of which were of widespread occurrence in Europe, could be grouped into ten main types, on the basis of the plants they contained and especially those which made up their bulk.

The ten main peat types described by Tolpa are:

    lake and pond weed peats
    reed peats
    large sedge peats
    brown moss and small sedge peats
    mineral bog moss peats
    aquatic bog moss peats or bog pool peats
    true bog moss peats
    alder wood peats
    birch wood peats
    pine wood peats.

All these types of peat may be found in Ireland, and Appendix 1 gives a list of all the main plants the immortal remains of which have gone to make up this vast natural resource which has both cursed and blessed the country.

Now having found out something about the nature of peat, perhaps the next question to answer is, what is a bog?

Ask anyone in Ireland the same question and they would be able to give you at least some sort of answer. What is more they would probably be able to name most of the bogs in their locality. However, their definition would certainly not include lakes, marshes, reedswamps, fens, callows and the like, so it would not include all the peat and peatland types described by Tolpa. So what exactly is a bog? In an attempt to answer this question we will take a look at peat formation in a locality which all the locals would agree used to be Pollagh Bog.

The Story of Pollagh Bog
On the southern flanks of the Hill of Usnagh, which legend has it is the centre of Ireland and from the summit of which you can on a clear day see features of no less than twenty counties, there arises one of the headwaters of the River Brosna which drains through the Great Bog of Allen and eventually into the Shannon (see map, p. 47). At some time in the past, before the bog was there, and before the river had a name, its meanderings fed into a series of depressions in the underlying limestone which was sealed over with clay and hence was watertight. The clay had been laid down by the same glacier that deposited a limestone block on the Hill of Usnagh. Thus it was that around 9000 years ago a lake or series of small lakes fed with mineral-rich alkaline waters existed on the spot now marked on the maps as Pollagh Bog. In the shallow waters of the lake margins, pond weeds grew in abundance and together with a rich phytoplankton helped charge the waters with dissolved oxygen and feed an abundance of animal life. The oxygenated waters of the rills and waterfalls of the inflow and outflow streams must have provided ideal habitats for salmon

and sea trout to lay their eggs in safety, their progeny returning to the sea from whence they came.

In the shallow embayments of the lake, away from the main flow of water, conditions would have become stagnant, especially in a dry summer, providing the first anaerobic spots in which peat formation could commence, peat made up of the remains of pondweeds, waterlilies, millfoil and frogbit. The remains of these plants accumulated on the bottom of the lake until the water was shallow enough to allow the growth of *emergent perennial plants* such as bulrush, reedmace, pond horsetail and common reed. (Perennial means that they grow from year to year, and emergent means that their leaves, stems and flowers protrude above the surface of the water.) These plants created a veritable jungle of shoots, rhizomes and roots to slow the flow of water, to trap any material brought into the lake, and, when they died, to add to the peat-forming process speeding the infilling of the lake. Eventually the water became so shallow in places that the large perennial plants could no longer grow to perfection and so they were gradually replaced by smaller sedges and rushes which could thrive in less aquatic conditions. Bottle, acute, panicled and saw sedges mixed with black bog rush, greater spearwort and gipsywort, together with an abundance of what are best called brown mosses. These include the star mosses, spear mosses, feather mosses and scorpion mosses, and together they formed a carpet which could float on the surface at times of high water. In terms of peatland ecology this was a major point of change, for the surface of such a floating mat or *scraw* would soon be isolated from the main effects of water flowing through the system at all times of the year.

Throughout these early stages of peat formation, the accumulating silt and organic matter was in effect filling the lake basin and this reduced the volume of water contained in the primary lake. However, as the peat-producing vegetation spread across the lake it would have acted as a dam, slowing the flow, causing water to back up in the system and so increasing the surface area and hence the volume of water held in the lake. This process is known as *paludification*. Flowing groundwater is not only charged with minerals, including bicarbonates, washed and dissolved from the catchment, but also it can carry (or flush) away acidic and other products of the vegetation developing within the basin. So it was that up until the development of the floating mat stage the lake water and its peats had remained rich in minerals and neutral to alkaline in reaction.

As soon as the floating mat was well developed the surface vegetation was gradually elevated above the effects of groundwater flow and acidic and other products began to accumulate, changing the whole water chemistry of the system, a change rapidly mirrored by the make-up of the vegetation. Plants like bogbean and marsh cinquefoil became abundant, their long creeping shoots helping to stabilise the mat and providing conditions in which the slender sedge, yellow-beaked sedge, many-flowered bog cotton and certain bog mosses (*Sphagnum teres*,

27

S. recurvum and *S. subsecundum*) could begin to grow.

The new peat rich in bog moss that was now forming slowly but surely raised the surface of the vegetation above the reach of even the wildest fluctuations of the flowing groundwater: thus isolated, the final changes in the vegetation began to take place. Great swelling tufts or hummocks of other bog mosses (*Sphagnum papillosum, S. magellanicum, S. imbricatum, S. capillifolium* and *S. fuscum*) came to dominate the vegetation, their remains forming a reservoir of water perched above the original groundwater level and fed only by the rain falling directly on the surface. The acidifying powers of the bog mosses (see p. 24) now really came into play, for out of contact with the flowing mineral-enriched groundwater there was nothing to flush away or neutralise their acid products.

The whole habitat rapidly soured and only the most perfectly adapted plants survived the rigours of life on the high bog surface, plants like single-flowered bog cotton and deer sedge with their needle-like leaves and ability to retain and recycle minerals, and the full spectrum of the members of the heather flower family from ling, with its almost scale-like overlapping leaves, to the cranberry, creeping flat over the surface. The latter dominated the hummocks, especially where they tended to dry out and the bog mosses themselves gave way to lambswool moss, fork mosses, white fork moss, bank hair mosses and lichens. Members of the vegetation of the earlier phases could still be found growing in the wet hollows and pools between the hummocks. There mud sedge, white-beaked sedge, many-flowered bog cotton, bog asphodel and even bogbean grew on with reduced vigour on carpets of *Sphagnum cuspidatum* and *S. recurvum*.

It was in these wetter areas that the sundews must have first grown in their greatest abundance, the long-leaved and great sundews favouring the edges of the pools and wet carpets while the round-leaved sundew would have been able to grow even on the highest hummocks of *Sphagnum capillifolium*.

These wettest areas of this bog were also the home of Ireland's rarest bog plant, the Rannoch rush, first found growing by Father John J. Moore, Professor of Botany at University College Dublin and one of the world's leading peatland scientists. Although once quite widespread in Europe and with some ten stations in Britain and Ireland, it, perhaps more than any other peat former, has suffered from drainage and alteration of our boglands. Being totally dependent on the special features of the habitat which link the acid floating mat to the bog pool stage of development, it will be one of the first to be affected by drainage. Unfortunately, it is now thought to be extinct in Ireland, for the bog described above has been cut away. In Britain it now occurs only on Rannoch Moor in Perthshire, hence its common name, and in Europe it is becoming an increasingly rare species. Its Irish location on Pollagh Bog was even more precarious because the pools around which it grew were part of a soak system which led excess water from the surface of the bog through a natural drainage system which, when the bog was being developed for turf-cutting, was opened up and its habitat immediately destroyed.

So it was that in a matter of 9000 years an open lake fed by mineral-rich alkaline water overflowing with fish and wildfowl became the acid, red-brown mass of Pollagh Bog, of little interest to anyone except students of natural history and the prospectors of Bord na Móna.

As the story of Pollagh Bog shows, bogs develop in stages, each with its own characteristic plants or vegetation. These stages of development are preserved in layers of different peat types in the bog. The final stage or layer is, of course, easiest to see, as it is on top. In the case of Pollagh Bog it was there in all its damp, diverse glory in the 1950s, to be seen changing from season to season, a very special part of the living heritage of Ireland.

The rest of the story of the bog was unravelled by means of a series of borings down into the peat using a special instrument which could collect and retrieve a 'core' of peat for study in the laboratory. Microscopic examination of a series of such cores allowed Pollagh Bog to tell its own story to those members of the twentieth century with the will to listen and to learn, a story of 9000 years of natural history which changed the landscape, and as it did, went through the following seven main phases of peat development:

1. lake and pond weed peats
2. reed peats
3. large sedge peats
4. brown moss and small sedge peats
5. mineral bog moss peats
6. aquatic bog moss peats or bog pool peats
7. true bog moss peats

Now, these are seven of the main peat types described by Tolpa (see p. 26) for the whole of Europe, and they represent steps in an ordered succession of change, change brought about by the gradual accumulation of peat, slowly but surely altering key characteristics of the environment and habitat, the vegegation and the landscape.

STAGE 1: Development of peat mainly composed of truly aquatic plants in an open lake supplied with a large flow of mineral-rich groundwater. This brings not only dissolved minerals including bases into the system but also a certain amount of oxygen and silt in suspension. The peats so produced are therefore heavy and have no tendency to float on the water.

STAGE 2: The water is now shallow enough to allow the growth of the common reed which thrives on silty peat. The dense growth of the plants impedes and

Pl. 10 Vanishing lakes. . . Pond weeds
with floating leaves are in the process of
peat formation, a process that will
gradually change an open lake fed with
mineral-rich alkaline water into an acid,
nutrient-poor bog. Over the last 10,000
years countless lakes of all shapes and
sizes have gone the bogland way.

slows the flow of groundwater, less silt is brought into the system, stagnation begins to prevail at certain times of the year and lighter, less humified peats begin to form.

STAGE 3: Continued growth of the large perennial plants slows the water flow even further. They and the peat they help to form act as an effective barrier holding the water back so that the flow is no longer continuous to all parts of the basin.

STAGE 4: The lighter peats now dominated by smaller sedges and brown mosses are able to float on the surface at times of higher water. The main effect of the flowing groundwater is thus directed beneath a floating mat of vegetation.

STAGE 5: The developing dome of peat, its surface dominated by the acidifying bog mosses, is now raised above all but the wildest fluctuations of mobile groundwater. These, however, can still occur under extreme conditions of rainfall or snow-melt or if the water balance of the catchment is drastically altered in some way. At this stage large bogs may also develop their own internal drainage soaks through which water still flows.

STAGE 6: The dome of the bog moss peat by this stage has sufficient bulk to hold its own water table perched above all effects of mineral-rich or mineral-enriched flowing groundwater — a reservoir fed only by rain falling directly upon its surface. Two main types of peat are formed under these conditions, the aquatic bog moss peats and the true bog moss peats.

What Exactly is a Bog?

Now that we know a little about the ways in which the various types of peat are formed it is possible to get to grips with real definitions.

Peats of types 1 and 2 formed in open water conditions are best termed *lake peats*. Those of types 3 and 4 which are formed under the influence of flowing groundwater should be termed *fen peats* and the areas in which they form are called *fens*. Peats of type 5, being intermediate in nature between the true fens and the real bogs, are best called *poor fens*. The term *bog* is then restricted to peat and peatland types 6 and 7, aquatic bog moss peats and true bog moss peats.

A bog is thus any area of Ireland's (or of the world's) surface which is covered with peat whose only mineral supply is the rain and dust which falls directly on its surface and the flora and fauna it supports.

We have seen that seven of Europe's top ten peat types as described by Tolpa (see p. 26) were found in abundance in the profile of Pollagh Bog, the vast majority of which has now been cut away. What of the other three main types categorised by Tolpa, all of which are dominated by the remains of trees and other large woody plants:

11

12

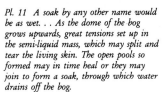

PETER FOSS

Pl. 11 A soak by any other name would be as wet. . . As the dome of the bog grows upwards, great tensions set up in the semi-liquid mass, which may split and tear the living skin. The open pools so formed may in time heal or they may join to form a soak, through which water drains off the bog.

Pl. 12 Lake today, bog tomorrow. . . An open lake fed by water draining from the hills will eventually become an extension of the bog which already forms its shore. The water is shallow enough for rooted plants with floating leaves and large rushes and sedges to grow. It is only a matter of time before the bog takes over.

Pl. 13 West is best for blanket bog. . . Western lowland blanket bog in late summer. Black bog rush and purple moor grass grow in tussocks on the hummocks and bogbean, sundews, sedges and bog asphodel grow around the shallow pools. This unique vegetation, for its exact counterpart is found nowhere else in the world, once covered 400,000 hectares of the wettest mildest parts of Ireland.

CAITRÍONA DOUGLAS

32

15

Pl. 14 *How to raise a bog. . .*
Hummocks of bog moss provide a head-above-water home for ling, cross-leaved heath and lichens, while pools and hollows do the same for the water-loving mosses and plants like bogbean. The bog hummocks grow up and, like a sponge, carry their own water with them. Eventually they may dry and die, as others rise up in the adjacent pools. The whole bog thus grows up to form a gigantic dome or cupola.

Pl. 15 *Unique combination. . .*
Carnation sedge growing on a sward of bog mosses — papillose, red and burgundy red. This, together with the heath-spotted orchid, makes a unique combination of plants found growing together only on bogs intermediate between the true raised and ridge-raised bogs of the central plain and the blanket bogs of the wetter west. The living surface of every bog has its own story to tell. Read all about it on pages 85-6.

CAITRÍONA DOUGLAS

Fen forest peats dominated by the remains of alder and willow with abundant remains of large sedges and *Sphagnum imbricatum*.

Poor fen forest peats dominated by the remains of birch and *Sphagnum palustre* and *S. magellanicum*.

True bog forest peats dominated by pine with abundant bilberry, *Sphagnum palustre* and *S. magellanicum*.

These *wood* or *forest peats* form when at some stage in the development of the fen, poor fen or bog, the conditions change so that the surface of the peat dries out sufficiently to be invaded by bushes and trees. Study of cores extracted from other peat bogs in central Ireland and of peat faces in cutaways have shown that the three basic types of forest peat did exist in the past.

So it is true to say that all the main types of peat found in Europe have developed on the central plain of Ireland. And not only in the far past, for in the days before Bord na Móna it was possible to follow the rivers as they wound their sinuous courses between the main lobes of the Bog of Allen and on the margins of pools, lakes and meanders to find many examples of all the types of peat-forming vegetation still extant and doing well — all, that is, except the last, true bog forest. Fortunately, in the wider context of the whole of Ireland, the same is still true. Examples of all the main types of peatland vegetation each with its own special Irish characteristics may still be found and marvelled at.

Recent surveys have shown that the vast majority of Ireland's peatlands are true bogs, a mere 9000 hectares being fens or poor fens. There are two reasons for this.

In the first place, mineral-rich or mineral-enriched peatlands are under the influence of flowing groundwater and so are close to natural rivers and streams; this would have made them easy to drain, which in turn would make them attractive to farmers. Also, their peat is rich in mineral nutrients, so they could readily and rewardingly be turned over to agriculture. Fens and poor fens would have been exploited agriculturally early on, their altered peat becoming improved leys (grazing lands) and even used for crops. The true bog peats, on the other hand, being more remote from the natural drainage system and with acid, nutrient-poor peats, offered little to tempt the landowner or tenant into expensive drainage and development. So in the main it is the true bog peats that have remained intact, except for domestic turf-cutting around their margins.

Secondly, as we shall see, not only at Pollagh but in the pervasively wet, warm, oceanic climate of Ireland, the natural landscape process has been to replace lakes, fens and poor fens with a coverall of acid bog peat — an overall acidification of vast tracts of the land long before acid rain was ever thought of.

Pl. 16 The biggest hummocks. . . This is Sphagnum imbricatum, *the bog moss which forms the largest hummocks on raised, ridge-raised, intermediate and blanket bogs. This handsome plant was much commoner in the past, when, along with the other bog mosses, it helped to form the bulk of the peat, which has helped to warm the hearths of Ireland over the centuries. As a hummock-former, it is more susceptible to the effects of fire, drainage and grazing and so today it is much rarer. The sword-shaped leaves of bog asphodel protrude through the living cover.*

So it is small wonder that when a local talks of 'the bog' he or she means the acid peatlands which have for so long stood in the way of Ireland's agricultural development.

Land of Peat and Bogs

The peat cover of Ireland was first surveyed between 1809 and 1814 and a detailed map was prepared, copies of which are now extremely rare and of great value. The object of the exercise was to assess the potential of the peatlands for agricultural use and exploitation. The survey showed that some 1.2 million hectares of Ireland were then covered with peat, that is something between one-sixth and one-seventh of its total land surface area. The survey distinguished three main types of bog, recording that somewhat more than half the area was covered with what they called *red* or *raised bogs* and low level or *lowland blanket bogs*, and somewhat less than half with *mountain blanket bogs*.

This survey lumped the raised bogs and the lowland blanket bogs together, because the object of that exercise was to ascertain their potential value to agriculture. It is obvious that the blanket bogs that developed on the uplands, often above the 300-metre contour, would be less amenable to agriculture than those that developed on the warmer lowlands. But in biological terms it is more sensible to group the *blanket* bogs, mountain and lowland, together and treat the *raised* bogs as a separate entity, although, as we shall discover, exact definitions, though easy to make, are not simple to uphold.

CHAPTER 2:
HOW TO RAISE A BOG

Blanket bogs are found in the wettest parts of the country, but the raised bogs are typical of the drier inland areas especially on the central plain, where they formed, as Pollagh Bog did, from lake basins and water-filled depressions with or without the complication of a supply of mineral-rich water brought in by a stream or river. However, in most cases the classic sequence is followed as lake and fen peats gave way to true bog peats which continue to grow upwards to form a dome or *cupola* of peat, hence the name raised bog.

Just how long this process can continue and just how high the dome of rain-fed peat can grow above the influence of the flowing groundwater depends on a number of factors, especially the climate and the annual march of rainfall and evaporation. If there are any long periods of the year in which water loss by evapotranspiration (evaporation from the water surface and via the plants) exceeds supply by precipitation (rainfall, snow etc) the development of the true peat dome will be limited.

However, as a mass of peat acts like a sponge, its area and volume also play an important role which must be taken into consideration. Capillary action within the peat mass will tend to hold the water up, against the force of gravity, which will act in exactly the opposite direction. The water table in the growing dome of peat must take the line of least resistance and so under perfect conditions it takes the form of a convex lens, highest in the middle and lowest around the margins. The shape of the dome follows and mirrors this to perfection unless, as in the case of Pollagh Bog, some physical feature obstructs or enhances the development. Pollagh Bog itself formed over a series of shallow lake basins set within the flood plain of the Brosna. The fen peat grew up and out and eventually covered the flood plain of the river. The cupola of the bog then grew up and lapped against the valley side, up which it continued to grow (see diagram p. 40).

So, within the constraints of climate, the ultimate height of the cupola will depend on the area of the bog. In essence, under similar climatic conditions, the larger the area the taller will be the dome of the raised bog and it is possible

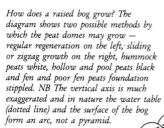

How does a raised bog grow? The diagram shows two possible methods by which the peat domes may grow — regular regeneration on the left, sliding or zigzag growth on the right, hummock peats white, hollow and pool peats black and fen and poor fen peats foundation stippled. NB The vertical axis is much exaggerated and in nature the water table (dotted line) and the surface of the bog form an arc, not a pyramid.

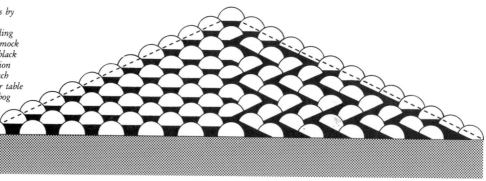

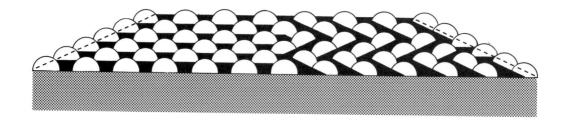

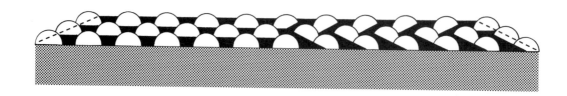

40

that at some time the tallest raised bog cupola in Ireland existed somewhere on the central plain.

If this was indeed the case, I am sure the honour would have gone to one of the lobes of the Great Bog of Allen, all of which, like Pollagh, itself an outlier of the system, began their existence in water-filled hollows in an undulating plain of glacial clay, flooded at times by water draining down into the Shannon. These giant domes of peat separated by tracts of callow — that is treeless fen peat bordering the rivers and streams and periodically inundated by water from the feeder rivers — must have presented a display of raised bogs bettered nowhere else on earth. Each dome of bog peat was between four and seven metres deep, had developed on some two to three metres of lake and fen peat and all were actively growing. That was until drainage schemes allowed the self-fertilising callow meadows to be turned into managed pastures for the grazing of cattle or fields for the raising of crops, and peat-cutting inexorably began to destroy these true wonders of the peatland world. Much of this destruction was unfortunately accomplished before they were surveyed in the detail they deserved, so we can only guess which held the Irish and possibly the world record. If I were a betting man I would plump for one of the sections of the Blackwater complex, which rose at least 5.9 metres above its mineral edge on the western side surveyed, using a dumpy level, by myself in 1956. This bog is in fact the largest in area shown in the 1814 survey with an estimated 6000 acres of exploitable peat. However, it must be noted that the giant cupola was divided into two sub-equal halves by the Gowlan River, so again its effective area was not much more than Pollagh Bog itself.

In such a basin which has a large catchment area of its own and especially when it is fed by a river or stream, the growth of the cupola of peat is further complicated. The process of back flooding *(paludification)* caused by the blockage of streams and rivers may continue to promote the development of fen and poor fen peats in those parts of the basin subject to groundwater flow or to periodic flooding. The dome of true bog peat may thus be totally or partly surrounded by actively growing fen and poor fen, best described by the Scandinavian term *lagg*. The whole complex is then termed a 'domed raised bog with marginal lagg'. Long after the dome of bog peat has started to develop, continued growth of the fen peat in the lagg may raise the basal groundwater level in the basin, above which the dome of peat will continue to develop. The whole complex then continues to grow in unison, until eventually all factors begin to balance out, peat growth slows down and bushes and trees invade the fen bog complex. The rarity of both fen and bog forest (which can only partially be explained by agricultural exploitation) is living proof that active peat growth is still in the ascendancy clear across Ireland.

How do the Great Red Domes Grow?

The fact that many of the main peat-forming plants and especially the bog mosses grow in large swelling tufts or hummocks, each not unlike miniature raised bogs both complicates and complements the growth process.

The main peat formers, *Sphagnum papillosum, S. magellanicum, S. capillifolium, S. imbricatum* and *S. fuscum,* demonstrate this ability for anyone to see and large hummocks of the latter two species, though now uncommon, were main features of the great red bogs. The largest I ever saw and measured was a monster hummock of *Sphagnum imbricatum* 1.24 metres in height with an overall basal area of 14 square metres. It was undoubted king of the cupola of the bog mentioned above as being a contender for the Irish and perhaps the all-comers record.

It stands to reason that, despite their ability to hold water, the taller a hummock grows the more susceptible will its surface be to the vagaries of summer drought, fire and drainage. This may well explain the fact, recorded both in Ireland and in many other parts of western Europe, that although the remains of the two hummock-formers, *S. imbricatum* and *S. fuscum,* are abundant in the peat, in places almost to the exclusion of all others, they are less abundant as members of the contemporary bog flora.

Whatever the exact explanation for this all the large hummocks studied in the 1958 survey (see box) showed signs of a drying process, their tops and sides becoming invaded by ling and by mosses, bank hair mosses, fork mosses, especially white fork moss, and by lichens. The white fork moss *Leucobryum glaucum* is of great interest, for though it is not a true bog moss the structure of its leaves bears some resemblance to those of the *Sphagna* and they act as an efficient sponge, holding their own reservoir of water.

However, replacement of the dominant bog mosses with other species less well adapted to bog life leads to die-back, breakdown and eventual collapse of the hummock. The dying hummocks may then merge back into the general bog surface. This surface is made up of lawns, hollows and open pools and is dominated by other bog mosses, which, having a smaller water-holding capacity, do not have the ability to grow up into hummocks. These include, from the most to the least aquatic, *Sphagnum cuspidatum, S. pulchrum, S. papillosum* and *S. tenellum,* which occur around pools and hollows.

This surface pattern of hollows and lawns and building, aging and collapsing hummocks is termed the *regeneration complex* and is linked to the method by which the cupola grows upwards. The theory is that as one hummock grows up too high above the water table and dies and collapses, another will rise up nearby adding its own capillary mass to the process. So, slowly but surely, the surface of the bog will grow upwards, as it were dragging the water table behind. Studies of bog profiles have in many cases revealed a series of peats made up of hollow and hummock communities perched one on top of the other, lending

Analysis of 250-metre-square samples recorded from a series of active raised bog on the central Irish plain indicated the following order of importance of the bog mosses in terms of percentage living cover:

S. papillosum	26%
S. capillifolium	24%
S. magellanicum	23%
S. cuspidatum	14%
S. imbricatum	7%
S. fuscum	3%
S. pulchrum	1%
S. subnitens	1%
S. tenellum	0.3%
S. subsecundum	0.05%

The survey, made in 1958, relegates the importance of our *Sphagnum imbricatum* and *S. fuscum* to around ten per cent and yet in many places on the same bogs *S. imbricatum* made up ninety per cent of the upper layers of the peat. Two explanations must be taken into consideration to account for this apparent change. Firstly, of all the bog mosses the remains of *S. imbricatum* are the easiest to identify in the peat and hence may have been over-represented in the survey. Secondly, all the bog cupolas may be approaching their climax heights and the reduction of *Sphagnum fuscum* and *S. imbricatum* is due to natural changes associated with the slowing of growth and drying of the bog surface.

weight to this theory.

However, it is just as likely that the whole peat mass acts as a capillary sponge 'drawing' the water table upwards. The hummocks and hollows playing a less active role simply maintain station or wander back and forth across the cupola as it grows. Whichever mechanism is taking place, any sudden shift in the water balance of the peat dome or the water catchment which feeds the bog will be put on record, either as a *flooding horizon* ('horizon' here meaning a band or layer in the peat, visible in cross-section) made up mainly of hollow peats or a *standstill horizon* made of highly humified hummock peats rich in lichens.

Examination of peat profiles in many parts of Europe shows that both of the suggested mechanisms of growth have taken place in the past and by inference are still taking place today. It also shows many other features less easy to explain.

43

Bog Pools

The whole sequence of bog development is further complicated by growth of algae in the pools. Inspection of large hollows and pools, especially in summer, will often reveal a blanket-like mat of an alga called *Zygogonium ericitorum*, together with colonial desmids and strands of a tiny leafy liverwort called *Cladopodiella fluitans*. Sorry about the name, but it is a very beautiful, almost microscopic plant whose bifid leaves (each like a tiny crab's claw) turn dark magenta black and so stand out from the matrix of yellow bog moss.

This dark coloration is in all probability a reaction of the plant to the high intensities of light in the open pools. Although the process of photosynthesis, and hence the whole aerobic living world, is dependent on light, too much light can damage the photosynthetic machinery. Many plants react by putting up the shutters in the form of other pigments, which help block out the harmful rays. The bog mosses themselves are masters of the art, and inspection of large hummocks, especially of the more gaudily coloured species, will reveal the deepest coloration on the sunniest side of the hummock. In the same way, when colourful species like *Sphagnum capillifolium* and *S. magellanicum* are found growing in shady situations they appear blanched and are therefore easily confused with *Sphagnum palustre*.

Meanwhile, back to the pools in the height of summer: the mat of algae and *Cladopodiella* may often be covered with bubbles of oxygen. Such high concentrations of oxygen can promote a process termed *corrosive oxidation*, which retards and impedes the accumulation of peat and so will keep the pool open until overgrowth by other species around the margin shades it and eventually fills it in. Study of such pools in Scandinavia and more recently in County Mayo has shown that oxidative conditions have arrested the process of peat formation, in some cases for more than 2000 years, slowing and complicating the growth of the bog. However, these extreme forms of oxidation have mainly occurred in pools enriched with minerals.

So you see, the process of bog development is indeed a complex one, and examination of many peat faces in cutaways across Ireland indicates that both patterns of regeneration and all permutations and combinations of patterns have taken place in the past and by inference are still taking place today.

Tension on the Dome

The cupola of a raised bog is in effect a gigantic drop of water held together by a matrix of dead, partly decayed plant remains, held intact by a living skin of peat, forming plant communities the patterning of which reflects the growth process. As the dome grows in height and the slope increases, all sorts of tensions begin to develop in the peat, and cracks and tears may appear on the surface. Under normal conditions, development of these tensions will be very gradual, manifesting on the living skin as elongate pools running across the main angle of a slope. These pools will immediately become colonised by the most aquatic of the bog mosses and will form elongate hollows dominated by *Sphagnum cuspidatum*. The pools will be enriched by minerals released from the breakdown of peat and may become focal centres for drainage and for visiting birds and animals who will further enrich their waters, and so they are often colonised by algal mats.

On a perfect dome of peat such tension pools will be arranged more or less concentrically around the highest point, a feature that is very common in Scandinavia, where the term *kermi* bog is used. On more irregular cupolas and especially on the elongate, often lopsided domes typical of the Bog of Allen, the tension features are more complex, but where they exist they are always arranged across the main angle of slope. From the air the normal irregularities of the hummock — hollow regeneration complex are difficult to see unless the sunlight catches them in exactly the right direction, but the more regular tension zone features stand out at all times.

The Pollagh Soak — How did it Form?

Another striking feature of the surface of most of the larger bogs are more massive internal drainage features called *droggs* (another Scandinavian term) or more commonly in Ireland *soaks*. A soak is easily spotted, for the vegetation is very different from that of the rest of the bog surface, and is often dominated by grasses, shrubs and bushes. A soak is in effect a valley which is being cut into the peat by flowing water. Soaks are full of holes and pitfalls and so are very difficult to traverse. A large dome of peat even in an average year will intercept an enormous amount of water. Pollagh Bog, for example, would receive a staggering 4.5 billion litres, although of course it doesn't fall all at once, and without it the bog wouldn't exist. When the dome is fully charged with water any extra must be shed from its surface. This will take place either by drainage downslope and from the margins or via some internal drainage system, and that is how the soaks are formed.

It was around one such soak that the Rannoch rush once grew in abundance on Pollagh Bog. The soak ran from a point high on the cupola north-west across the bog to drain into the cutaways near the village of Pollagh. There is little doubt that before the destruction of the north margin of the bog prior to the building of the Grand Canal, the soak continued in its course to be lost in the callows flanking the Brosna river.

The presence of birch trees — all less than two metres tall — around the head of the soak and of drier communities dominated by ling and single-flowered bog cotton along its margins could indicate that the cupola is approaching its maximum height, because a slowing down in the rate of peat growth and speeding up in the rate of peat breakdown would enrich the surface enough to allow the growth of the trees. Other indications of nutrient enrichment are the occurrence of common sedge, bottle sedge, sweet vernal grass, narrow buckler fern and *Juncus kochii* in the soak, all of which are more typical of fen systems. Mineral enrichment of the drainage waters must also partially account for the luxuriant growth of purple moor grass lower in the soak. The tussocky form of this plant, which is typical of fen and poor fen, is also indicative of a fluctuating water table.

Another explanation could be that the pools at the head of the soak act as focal points, attracting visiting animals and especially birds like snipe and Greenland white-fronted geese, their presence and activity disturbing and enriching the area with nutrients.

The Rannoch Rush Story

Despite much searching (see pl. 20), the unmistakable rhizomes of the Rannoch rush have so far only been found in the peat of Pollagh Bog down to a depth of 80cm and, at one place only, down to a depth of 175cm. This suggests that it is a recent introduction. Recent, that is, if you put the early Christian period into that category, for this would appear to be the date of the earliest of this peat. As it seems unlikely that even early Christians would have introduced this plant on purpose, all we can do is assume that seeds of the Rannoch rush were introduced on the mud or peat which caked the feet or feathers of visiting birds. Finding the conditions ideal for its growth, it colonised the area and remained marooned, as it were, on Pollagh Bog for at least the past 1500 years (see diagram page 48).

There is a peculiar depression at the head of the soak where the peat rich in the rhizomes of the Rannoch rush descends as a plug down to a maximum depth of 175cm. Vertically beneath this is a plug of *marl* (limey, mineral-rich soil) protruding up from the clay seal and marking the position of a mineral-rich spring, which must have bubbled up into the original lake. The presence of woody peat at the top of this calcareous (limey) plug suggests the development of a spring-fed fen at this point: such spring-fed fens of a metre or more in height are not uncommon. They are composed of calcareous deposits, tufas and marls, which build up until they counterbalance the hydrostastic pressure of the spring, when they are rapidly invaded by bushes and trees, the mineral-rich spring water continuing to flow from the margins.

As the basal fen peats grew up they would in time have engulfed the mound and suppressed the flow of spring water, perhaps creating a point of weakness in the developing peats above. Now, if spring water could flow through the clay seal at this point it stands to reason that as the head of water built up in the new peat layers above, water could also have flowed the other way, that point on the bog becoming a focal centre for drainage. This downflow of water would account for the depression of all peat strata at that point and for the massive accumulation of the remains of the Rannoch rush at the bottom of the funnel.

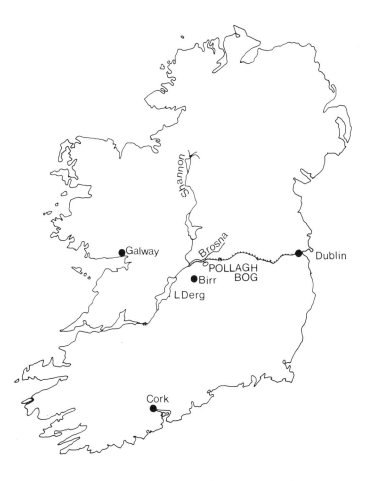

Similar funnel-shaped depressions have been found on bogs in Europe and a classic one on the Grundlenried in south Germany receives all the water which drains from an extensive soak, the vegetation of which is also dominated by *Sphagnum cuspidatum*, Rannoch rush, mud sedge and yellow-beaked sedge.

The head of the Pollagh soak was underlain by a narrow wedge of peat made up of the remains of the saw sedge, a plant characteristic of the edges of lakes and of fens. This overlies peats rich in woody remains which themselves developed on top of the peats typical of an acid bog cupola. Please take a careful look at the diagram (page 48) based on the work of Fr Moore. It looks as if just as that section of the bog was beginning to dry out enough to support the growth of

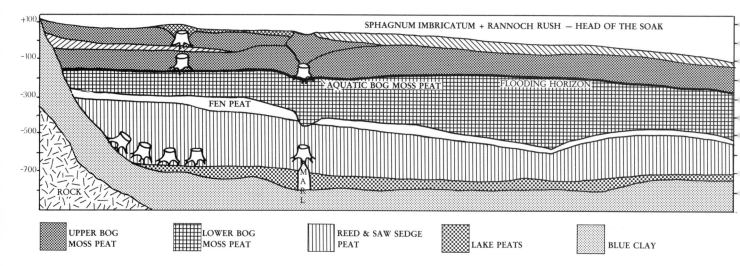

SPHAGNUM IMBRICATUM + RANNOCH RUSH — HEAD OF THE SOAK

AQUATIC BOG MOSS PEAT

FLOODING HORIZON

FEN PEAT

MARL

ROCK

| UPPER BOG MOSS PEAT | LOWER BOG MOSS PEAT | REED & SAW SEDGE PEAT | LAKE PEATS | BLUE CLAY |

trees it was flooded by mineral-rich water allowing the saw sedge to grow. Though the main effect of this 'fen' water terminated at the funnel-shaped depression, the effect of the 'flood' was carried on downslope producing the extensive layers of pool peat dominated by *Sphagnum cuspidatum* at the head of the soak.

This in essence is what may well have happened. As the bog cupola developed, it lapped against and grew up the slope of the mineral ground which bounds its south-eastern flank on which is now situated the village of Derrycooly. As the surface of the cupola rose up towards the 60-metre mark and beyond, something happened to concentrate water onto the bog surface. Perhaps the trees on the catchment died, which would have caused an increase in run-off, or perhaps one of the streams now flowing round the bog was diverted and entrained. Either of these events could have been caused by natural or people-made phenomena. What exactly occurred we do not know, but the end result was a flooding of the upper section of the bog with mineral-rich water initiating the growth of the saw sedge peat and the other changes recorded in the bog profile, and providing an ideal habitat for the growth of the Rannoch rush.

Something similar happened at another soak, on the cupola of Lower Newtown Bog, which forms a watershed between the Little Brosna and the Rapemills River. The dome of peat rises up from the callow bordering the Rapemills to lap up onto the mineral ground which flanks the bog. From this edge a very distinct tongue of vegetation stretches towards the centre of the bog. The vegetation is dominated by birch and willow with the following indicators of mineral enrichment being present: sweet vernal grass, star sedge, bottle sedge, marsh pennywort, smooth rush, purple loosestrife, marsh cinquefoil, purple moor grass, broad buckler fern, royal fern and the moss *Bryum pseudotriquetrum*. Study of the surface contours indicates how, before the marginal peat-cutting, water could have flowed onto the surface of the bog from the mineral catchment.

A magnificent soak, probably the best now left in Ireland, bisects the cupola of Clara Bog, one of the great lobes of the Bog of Allen. Work is at present under way to try to understand the method by which it was formed and the mechanism which maintains its fenlike character.

In any case, thanks to Fr Moore's work, recorded for posterity in the *Irish Naturalists' Journal,* we know that flooding occurred on the upper part of our soak on Pollagh Bog; we don't know, however, whether this flooding was partly caused by human activity, but we do know that humans had something to do with such flooding in other places. Many instances are recorded of ditches that were cut to drain a bog having in fact worked in the opposite direction, channelling water instead onto the bog surface. At Wynbunbury Moss in England, for instance, which is now a national nature reserve, a drain was cut, at some time in the past, towards the centre of the bog. The result was not to drain the acid bog but to channel mineral-rich water towards its heart, initiating the growth of a large stand of saw sedge in the midst of the acid communities. It happened at Wynbunbury, so it could have happened at Pollagh, providing ideal conditions for the establishment of the Rannoch rush.

The key question about the Ranoch rush remains unanswered: why did it stay put on Pollagh? If it arrived there by chance, why couldn't chance have carried its seeds to the other nearby bogs, with 1500 years at its disposal? In the absence of any proof, all I can do is advance an educated guess. One constant feature of all the bogs of Ireland is the presence of another species which plays a very similar ecological role to the Rannoch rush. Its name is the bog ashpodel, a member of the lily family. It is one of those plants so typical of Ireland which are best called *oceanic,* which means that they only occur in areas near the seaboard of the continent. Over the major range of the Rannoch rush on the continent, bog ashpodel is not found. Could it be that the two are in some way mutually exclusive? In the majority of the vegetation samples listed by Fr Moore which include the Rannoch rush, bog ashpodel is absent. Did the flooding of this section of the bog simply tip the balance in favour of the new invader, allowing it to get its only foothold in Ireland? Unfortunately, now we will never know.

Layers in the Peat
Inspection of the peat faces in any cutaway will reveal the tell-tale patterns of the hummock and hollow peats, although it requires some degree of expertise to recognise them for what they are. Flooding horizons like that described above are more easy to recognise, although in many cases difficult to explain. Most common are extensive layers of pool peat, that is peat made up mainly of *Sphagnum cuspidatum.* These may extend right across the bog cupola. The most logical explanation would appear to be a rejuvenation of bog growth caused by some factor, external or internal.

Where such flooding or recurrence horizons have been found in many bogs over a large geographical area, they have usually been thought to be due to major climatic change. The most famous and widespread of these is the so-called *Grenzhorizont* (the border horizon), thought to be a reaction to a period of increasing wetness of climate which took place across Europe around 600 BC.

It would appear that under the drier conditions prevailing before that time, the growth of many of the bogs had slowed down, their surfaces becoming invaded by lichens, shrubs and even trees. Their slowly growing peats, being subject to long periods of water stress (i.e. lack of water) each summer, were so well decomposed that they were very dark in colour and only their toughest components could be recognised. A change to a wetter climatic regime put new life into the bogs, 'flooding' their surfaces with new well-preserved peat made mainly of *Sphagnum cuspidatum*. This layer of *precursor peat*, as it came to be known, stood out in marked contrast to the brown humified peats below and to the new more rapidly growing *S. imbricatum* peats above.

This division of the peat into the upper and lower *Sphagnum* peat is well known to turf-cutters and their donkeys. The upper layers, which are very light and so are easy to carry, are called 'white', 'flow' or 'fum' and are of little use as fuel. The lower heavier 'black' peat is ideal as a fuel — volume for volume it gives much more heat and is almost ash free. It is also a relatively non-polluting fuel, for, like all the other minerals, sulphur is in short supply in the peat and hence its combustion does not generate vast amounts of sulphur dioxide as does most coal.

The difference in consistency between the basal fen peats and the lower and upper bog moss peats can cause all sorts of strange and important phenomena to occur. For a start, depending upon its consistency and density, peat is able to expand and contract, compensating at least in part for the fluctuations in the water table, and thereby avoiding flooding of the surface during torrential rain or rapid snow-melt and drying of the surface during periods of drought. Moreover, it seems that in the development and growth of a bog, the various major layers can become separated from each other. This is because of differential flotation; in other words the layers have different densities and hence different floating abilities. This separation of the layers produces a layer of peaty water, which may act like a safety valve or perhaps a better term would be a compensating reservoir. Under normal conditions when the whole peat dome is charged with water, the lighter upper peat floats on top of the hidden reservoir. However, in periods of water loss, the floating peat would slowly settle down, the reservoir compensating for the water loss, and the surface would remain wet thus allowing the peat to continue to grow.

Liquid Cores and Bog Bursts
The most famous examples of raised bogs with a liquid compensating core reservoir are in County Tyrone. The Fairy Water Bog lies in the valley of the Fairy Water River and has, like Pollagh, developed on the flood plain now partly protected

by the meanderings of the river. The most outstanding feature of the bog is that large tracts of its active surface display abundant hummocks of *Sphagnum imbricatum*, which may be how many other Irish bogs looked in earlier times or at earlier stages of development. Borings taken below the regeneration complex revealed the presence of a reservoir of water at least two and a half metres deep, separating the dense fen peat below from the lighter bog peats above. Michael Morrison, who first described the bog, thought that such a hidden reservoir could compensate for water loss from the surface of the bog and suggested that it alone could account for the abundance of *S. imbricatum* on the bog surface as it is today. At no time would the floating surface of the mire have become dry enough to suppress the hummock-forming mosses or to allow them to dry enough to be killed by fire.

Other similar bogs have been described by scientists, such as Derrandoran Bog also in County Tyrone, Garry Bog in County Antrim, Borth Bog in Cardiganshire in Wales and Thorne Waste in Yorkshire in England. Other such bogs existed in the past and newspapers and local histories are littered with accounts of bog bursts or flows which themselves littered the valleys with the low density, highly buoyant flow peats and caused much devastation and even death.

Robert Lloyd Praeger, one of Ireland's foremost natural historians, records one such bog burst in his famous book *The Way that I Went*:

It was on peat-covered hills near Gneevgullia, out to the north-east of Killarney, that there occurred, three days after the Christmas of 1896, an extensive bog-burst that attracted much attention on account of the tragic circumstances accompanying it, a family of eight persons, their home, and their live-stock, having been carried away and buried. These bog-bursts or bog-slides are not very uncommon in Ireland, on account of the great prevalence of peat-bogs in the country. In certain conditions, the lower layers of a bog may become so highly charged with water that under the pressure of the superincumbent mass they gush out at the lowest point of the floor, dragging the wreck of the more solid upper layers after them. If the bog be large and deep, a great flood of semi-liquid matter may be ejected: and should the slope below the point of ejection be steep, a devastating torrent may result. Unwise turf-cutting, by producing a high face without due preliminary draining, has been frequently the cause of these accidents. It was so in the fatal Kerry case; the face of the turf-cutting gave way, and a vast mass of peat and water precipitated itself down the valley, the flood ceasing only when it entered the Lower Lake of Killarney, fourteen miles distant. When the flow finally died down, about a week after the outburst, a great saucer-shaped depression, at its deepest no less than forty-five feet below the former slightly convex surface, showed the amount of the extruded material. This, with the abundant stumps of pine which it had contained, was spread for miles over the lands below, the width of the covering varying according to the slope of the valley sides. "The flood has left behind it, in the upper portion of the valley," says a contemporary account, "a deposit of peat averaging three feet in thickness, here as everywhere contrasted by its black colour with the grassland or other surface on which it rests. Its compact convex margin, like that of outpoured oatmeal porridge, often two feet in height, serves equally well to define it; so that it was an easy task to determine and map the high-water level of the flood. The surface of the deposit was everywhere broken by great roots and trunks of Scotch Fir, which, in their enormous numbers, bore convincing testimony to the evisceration which the bog had undergone. The appearance of this sea of black peat, with its protruding stumps of black trees, was a sight melancholy in the extreme." The evacuated area showed a depression three-quarters of a mile long and broad; the upper crust had broken away along a series of concentric cracks as the lower layers rushed out, and thousands of floes a yard or more thick went careering down the valley, to be stranded here and there; the centre of the area of movement was swept bare down to the gravelly drift on which the bog had rested; near the edges, the heather-covered floes still lay about, getting more numerous and closer together till the margin of the firm bog was reached, where the cracks could be seen in all incipient stages. I had ample opportunities for studying this disastrous bog-burst for I was one of a small party, headed by W.J. Sollas, who a few days after the occurrence hurried down from Dublin to investigate on behalf of the Royal Dublin Society. It was dark cold weather, the Reeks were white with snow, the district a rather desolate one, and I well remember the feeling of depression with which we gazed at that black slimy mass stretching down the valley, somewhere in which lay entombed the bodies of Cornelius Donnelly, his wife and his six children.

There are records of at least twenty or twenty-five bog-slides in Ireland, dating from the beginning of the eighteenth century, and others have certainly occurred even within that period. As regards the extruded material, all traces of it soon vanishes, for when it has dried it makes excellent fuel, sometimes at the people's very doors! But the characteristic saucer-like depression in the bog may last long, and several times, tramping the Irish hills, I have come across the site of an unrecorded burst, often visible at a distance by the more abundant growth of Ling, which rejoices in the better drainage which it finds there.

When Professor Sollas and I looked into the question of bog-slides in 1896, we found that more occurrences of the sort appeared to have been recorded from Ireland than from all the rest of the world. They are certainly an especially Irish phenomenon; we have a kind of "corner" in bog-slides, and it behoves us to make the most of them. It is satisfactory, then, to find that such as have occurred in the last forty years have been duly investigated and reported on. The actual proximate cause of bog-slides is not always obvious, and no doubt differs in different cases. They happen mostly during the winter half of the year, as might be expected. Springs under a bog, increasing the liquidity of the interior, may be responsible: heavy rain, by increasing the weight of the cover, may prove the "last straw"; seismic movement has also been suggested.

Mostly the envelope would retain the semi-fluid mass were that envelope continuous: but turf-cutting or sometimes a natural scarp often provides a line of weakness. I remember George Francis Fitzgerald accounting for the large number of local bog-flows by the suggestion that the frequency of political tremors in Ireland shook the bogs down the mountain-sides; but he thought that a grave objection to this theory lay in the fact that only three had been recorded from Ulster!

So flows the bog, especially if it has a self-regulatory liquid centre. One can only wonder how widespread such phenomena were before peat-cutting, nibbling away at the edges of the bog, drained their liquid cores and relegated them to a state of declining senescence. We know that the bogs went into decline as the peat shows a decline in the abundance of the king of the peat formers, *Sphagnum imbricatum*.

It is interesting to speculate how such a liquid core could develop. From the example of Pollagh Bog there is no reason to doubt that flooding of the bog surface from the surrounding catchment at a certain stage in its development could initiate massive change, separating two existing peat layers. However, it seems more likely that this would cause a focus of weakness and initiate a bog burst or the development of a soak rather than the development of a core reservoir.

A more likely explanation of such a hidden reservoir is that a split could develop as part of the natural process of the growth of the bog. As the upper, lighter peat layer and the whole dome reach some critical mass, flotation could detach the upper layers producing the reservoir which itself would help regulate further growth. Whatever the exact mechanism, there is no doubt that a split would be most likely to develop at the interface between two layers, the lower of which had the remains of deep-rooting trees, bushes or shrubs binding the peat together and therefore holding it down. Such an explanation would seem especially likely in the cases of Fairy Water and Garry Bogs, where the reservoir sits on top of a layer of reed peat rich in woody remains. Praeger's description of the numerous pine stumps and trunks revealed by the bog burst of 1897 would also point to a similar basal layer held down by old tree roots.

There is one further explanation which must be taken into account and that relates to the rapid development of a bog in a steep-sided lake basin, the classic case being a closed basin which has neither permanent inflow nor outflow streams. In such a situation, after initial and limited development of some fen peat, mineratrophic bog peat develops rapidly as a skin floating on the surface of the water. The floating bog develops from the margins towards the centre, the area of open water gradually being obliterated by the developing mat. One of the most famous examples of this type of development is at Chartley Moss national nature reserve in Staffordshire, England. Here a large lake has disappeared under a floating mat of bog mosses dominated in places by stands of semi-mature pine forest. There you can have the singular experience of jumping up and down on the floating bog surface and making the trees round about rock back and forth. It is an amazing place, for the whole forest is supported on a peat raft some two metres deep floating over more than ten metres of water.

One similar bog in an early stage of development is in County Westmeath. Its name is Scragh Bog and again in Praeger's words, 'One of the best places is the "Scraw Bog", a long narrow lake entirely covered by a floating skin of vegetation over which one can walk (or perhaps more properly, wade) among a profusion of Round-Leaved Wintergreen, in Ireland found only in this neighbourhood.' In time deposition from the base of such a floating mat could at least partially fill the lake and then under the right conditions of climate grow up carrying the hidden reservoir with it to form a floating dome.

Different Sorts of Raised Bog

Bogs are amazing things and raised bogs are the most amazing of all; each is in effect a giant living organism growing from birth through adolescence and maturity to senescence. (Whether a bog actually dies is a matter of conjecture. Its growth can slow and stop, its surface being colonised by trees. However, a change in its water balance could set growth in motion once again.) A bog's bulk and the by-products of its life processes change both itself and the environment in which it develops. Like all living things, each one, though made up of the same component parts, is an individual and so all degrees of development and all permutations and combinations of the various features, hummocks and hollows, tension pools, regeneration complexes, soaks, floating layers and hidden reservoirs may be found. Each raised bog has its own story to tell, and of all the types of living system found on earth they record the history of their development in the most intricate organic detail.

Strange to relate, we cannot say with absolute certainty that any truly classic *contained* raised bogs have ever existed in Ireland. (That is raised bogs which have remained contained within the lake basins in which they had their origin.) Those that have survived are mostly of the *ridge-raised* and *flood-plain* variety in which growth of the cupola is not restricted to the basin in which it originated but has continued engulfing low ridges to coalesce with other cupolas developing in adjacent basins. The place to look for classic contained bogs would undoubtedly be along the drier eastern part of the country. However, although the names of towns and villages indicate the existence of red bogs in their vicinity, the bogs after which they were probably named have long since been so altered by cutting and drainage that no firm conclusions can be drawn. The best contenders to the title of true raised bogs so far described by naturalists are Fallahogy in County Derry, Ballyscullion in Country Antrim and Red Bog in County Louth (see pp 121-8).

All the rest would appear to be of the 'uncontained' type which are best referred to as ridge-raised bogs, which are intermediate between classic raised and classic blanket bogs. The vast bulk of the domed raised bogs, though in the main initiated and developed within basin sites, include those, like the lobes of the great Bog of Allen, which spread out from their basins to cover large areas of the flood plains of the rivers. Wherever possible they have also grown up around and over intervening low mineral ridges to form great complexes which are intermediate both in their morphology and in their climatic requirements between true raised and true blanket bogs.

Types of bog

in cross-sections (left) + plan views (right)

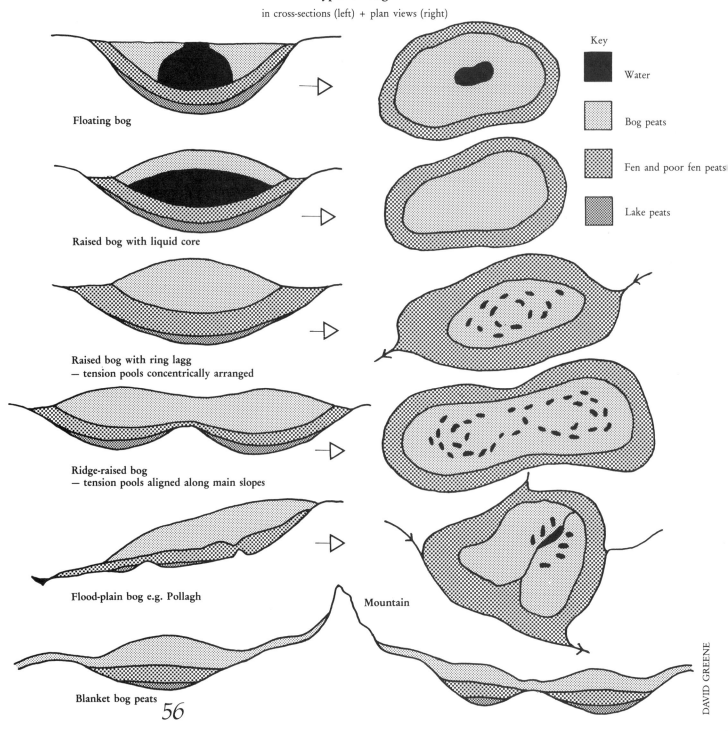

Floating bog

Raised bog with liquid core

Raised bog with ring lagg
— tension pools concentrically arranged

Ridge-raised bog
— tension pools aligned along main slopes

Flood-plain bog e.g. Pollagh

Mountain

Blanket bog peats

Key

Water

Bog peats

Fen and poor fen peats

Lake peats

56

DAVID GREENE

CHAPTER 3:
THE WET BLANKET

Although we use the terms raised bogs and blanket bogs, it is difficult to find a feature or features which can be used to distinguish adequately between the two sorts of bog. Raised bogs, whether contained, flood-plain or ridge-raised, appear to have their origin in water-filled depressions, and development of their acid bog strata is always preceded by the development of fen peats. Even when raised bogs grow from one basin to another, fen peats appear to pave the way, a point made very forcefully in Frank Mitchell's superb book *The Shell Guide to Reading the Irish Landscape*.

Development of Blanket Bogs
The growth of blanket peat, on the other hand, need not be initiated in lake and basin sites, for it can be found directly overlying mineral soil and even bedrock with no intervening deposit of fen peat. Of course, this does not mean that no raised bogs, poor fens or fens are ever found in the blanket bog areas. Far from it — in those vast, peat-covered landscapes all the forms of peatlands represented in Ireland are to be found. They are, however, lost within — or perhaps a better term would be welded together by — true blanket peats which have formed, can form and are still forming directly on the mineral soil or bedrock, wherever it does not drain too freely. If the ground slopes too steeply then it will drain easily and so it is unlikely to be a site for the development of blanket peat. No two authorities seem to agree about the amount of slope a blanket bog will tolerate. Some say a ten per cent slope sets the limit, others put it at eighteen per cent, yet it is possible to find peat of more than two metres in depth eroding from twenty-five per cent slopes on the flanks of the Twelve Bens in County Galway. Eroding they may be now, but it stands to reason that they must have formed on that same slope at some time in the past, and study of the profile shows no change throughout its depth except for a slightly coarser peat richer in mosses at the base.

   Too little rain and the bogs can't grow, too much rain and the process of erosion may be initiated; and if the rain is concentrated in the wrong place, erosion can be rapid and catastrophic. The bog burst in County Kerry described by Praeger (pp 51-3) was in all probability from a raised bog with a liquid core set within a large area of blanket bog.

How Peat Forms on Limestone
Perhaps the most amazing development of blanket bog is found on some of the bare limestone areas for which Ireland is so famous. You remember that acidity is one of the outstanding features of boggy environments, so limestone, the very opposite of an acid soil, is the last place you would expect peat to form, but form it does. The Ben Bulben plateau in Sligo/Leitrim is covered with blanket peat growing with apparent ease both on the acid millstone grits and on the porous limestone rich in bases. In the Burren, Ireland's most famous block of limestone rock, we can see the process of peat formation starting in some places. Cushions of a number of mosses, but especially the handsome golden *Breutelia chrysocoma*, appear to be able to grow directly on the bare bedrock. As they grow they produce a pad of humus into which acid-loving plants like ling, ericas and even bearberry seed. Their feeding roots, shunning contact with the limestone beneath, turn upwards against their better nature (for it is the wont of most roots to grow down) drawing sustenance from the pad of humus.

Bogs Forming in a Wet Climate
The constancy of rainfall and humidity of the oceanic climate helps to produce and maintain acidity. Rainwater is by nature very slightly acid and with the help of effluents produced by human beings it has an even greater tendency towards such dyspepsia. The surface layers, especially of a well-draining soil or pad of humus will soon be *leached* of all bases, that is all the bases will have been washed down through the soil, leaving the top layers acid.

Under drier circumstances, this leaching could, at least in part, be counteracted, as evaporation brings water, together with those dissolved bases and other minerals, back up to the surface. However, evaporation and upward transport of minerals is not very common in our wet, oceanic climate, especially not in those areas of the country where it is rare to get more than twenty consecutive days without measurable rainfall. Even in the height of summer the winds blowing onshore from the ocean are saturated with water and evaporation from the soil is minimal. Throughout the areas of Ireland where rainfall is high the leaching process reigns supreme, removing the bases, nutrients and all soluble minerals down through the soil beyond the reach of the plant roots, and leaving the soil acid and poor in minerals.

The surface vegetation — be it grassland, woodland, heath or bog — does its best to keep the useful minerals and, to a lesser extent, the bases, in cycle; but it appears that in time the soil of all living systems developed in wet climates tends towards acidity. All, that is, except fens, which by definition are kept supplied with base-rich flowing groundwater.

The most extreme form of soil development of this type is known to the soil science trade as a *podsol* with *iron pan*. Leaching slowly but surely moves all useful minerals and bases down the soil out of reach of the roots. Those which are most soluble are lost entirely and go to enrich the flowing groundwaters, which allow fens to be fens and feed the fish of rivers and lakes. Others, like iron, are deposited low down in the profile cementing the soil particles together to produce a rust-coloured iron pan which may become so hard and so thick that neither tree roots nor water can penetrate it. The trees eventually die of mineral starvation, their roots flooded by the water which cannot escape. So, conditions ideal for the development of bog come into existence directly on the soil surface. Add to this a liberal amount of hard acid rocks and drift, including clay which is impermeable to water, and what have we got? Conditions which allow the blanket bogs to get up and grow; and haven't they done well!

Wet Wonderlands

Blanket bog peats cover around three-quarters of a million hectares of Ireland. Something over half of these are scattered on the uplands and mountain ranges; the rest swathe the wet west with a living blanket, the like of which is seen nowhere else on earth. Where mountains occur in the west, the cover and diversity of peat development is best described as 'terrain boggling'. The Germans have an even more descriptive word for it *Terrainbedeckendenmoore*.

The largest tracts of blanket bog revealed by the 1814 survey were The Great Divide — 25,926 hectares in eastern Mayo, Erris-Tyrawley — 68,850ha in north Mayo, and Connemara — 77,760ha in County Galway. Of course, none of these is a single unit. They span the whole countryside, a somewhat tattered, soggy blanket, interrupted by lakes and water courses with the barer bones of the countryside sticking through wherever steep slopes shed water too fast to allow the peat to grow.

To do these wonderlands of water and wetland justice, all I can do is bow to Praeger's descriptions. Of Erris he wrote:

From north to east of Achill lies the Barony of Erris, the wildest, loneliest stretch of country to be found in all Ireland. From Mallaranny you may walk for thirty miles to the giant cliffs of North Mayo, your foot need never leave the heather save that twice you cross a road, fenceless, winding like a narrow white ribbon through the endless brown bog. The western shore is low and broken, and the heather there often gives place to poor pasture or tillage, but mostly the peat descends to the sea and below it, so that you may see thickly scattered pine stumps standing up on the beach or out of the waves.

59

These tell of past forests swallowed up first by the bog and then the sea. Of Connemara:

There are two Connemaras. South of the Galway–Clifden road a vast bog-mantled granite moorland extends, undulating or flattish, sown with innumerable brown lakelets, and with a low indented coast-line which is a mere labyrinth of land and sea. Immediately north of the same road, from Oughterard westward, the tall bare quartzite domes and cones of Maam Turk and the Twelve Bens (one should avoid the meaningless corruption 'Pins') rise steeply, and other mountains formed of schist and gneiss continue the highlands northward to the beautiful fiord of Killery, where Mayo replaces Galway. Both regions of Connemara have their charm, but I am not sure that of the two I do not prefer the great brown bogland to the grey naked hills. There is something infinitely satisfying about these wide, treeless, houseless undulations, clothed with Heather and Purple Moor-Grass, so filled with lakes and so intersected by arms of the Atlantic that water entangled in a network of land becomes almost imperceptibly land entangled in a network of water, and only the presence or absence of the mauve Lobelia or of brown seaweed tells whether one is on a lakeshore or on a seashore. On a day of bright sky, when the hills are of that intoxicating misty blue that belongs especially to the west, the bogland is a lovely far-reaching expanse of purple and rich brown: and the lakelets take on the quite indescribable colour that comes from clear sky reflected in bog-water, while the sea-inlets glow with an intense but rather greener blue. On such a day the wanderer will thank his lucky star that it has brought him to Connemara.

Diversity amongst Uniformity

A blanket of peat, it all sounds eminently dreary and monotonous, even to the chronic botanist and peatnik. But it is not, for, as you can guess, if the small, self-built slopes of the raised bogs can cause all sorts of tensions, pools and internal drainage features, so too can the slopes up which the blanket peats so avidly grow. Springs, streams and even small rivers flow through and even onto the bog, providing an amazing diversity of vegetation. The real regeneration complex is never well developed on blanket peats. That doesn't mean that hummocks and hollows don't exist: they do, and must, for the full spectrum of bog mosses is present, each with its own inbuilt characters of habitat preference and growth form. If the peat is deep enough, and depth will depend on the angle of slope, the living skin put under tension will crack to produce elongate pools. These heal to form elongate hollows running at right angles to the slope. Under other conditions the whole peat mass may tend to slide downhill to produce a similar series of deep, steep-sided pools separated by strips of peat. The whole thing looks like sections of a giant step-ladder following the main drainage slope. Under these conditions, excess water will flow from one to another and this movement, together

19

Pl. 18 Living signposts. . . Pale butterwort, another bogland carnivore, cross-leaved heath, purple moor grass and bog asphodel growing on a carpet of papillose bog moss. The butterwort is another of the special lusitanian *plants and it only grows in the warmer wetter blanket-boggy west.*

Pl. 19 Drop in for tea — butter but no bread. . . The Irish or great butterwort traps insects on its sticky butter-yellow leaves and raises its violet flowers as much as 20cm above the blanket bogs in a few places in Cork and Kerry. One of the very special bog plants which locates the bog and the botanist.

HEATHER ANGEL

63

Pl. 20 RIP rare Rannoch rush. . . The Rannoch rush was first found in Ireland by Father John J. Moore, Professor of Botany at University College Dublin. It grew on Pollagh Bog, which was part of the great Bog of Allen. Its distinctive remains in the peat tell us that it had only grown on the bog for the past 1500 years. How it got there, we can only guess. It disappeared when the bog was drained and cut away. Officially declared extinct, it may still live on, undiscovered, on some other bog.

REV. J. MOORE

21

Pl. 21 *Cranberry gets its name from the shape of its flowers, which bear more than a passing resemblance to the head of a crane, complete with long beak. This member of the heather flower family keeps a low profile, creeping over the bog moss hummocks, and produces dark red berries, very tart to the taste.*

Pl. 22 *For two years the caterpillar of the emperor moth feeds on the bogland plants. It then spins an intricate silken case at the top of the heather shoots, inside which it changes into an adult to start the cycle off once more. The target spots on its wings deflect the beaks of marauding birds away from its more vital parts.*

22

65

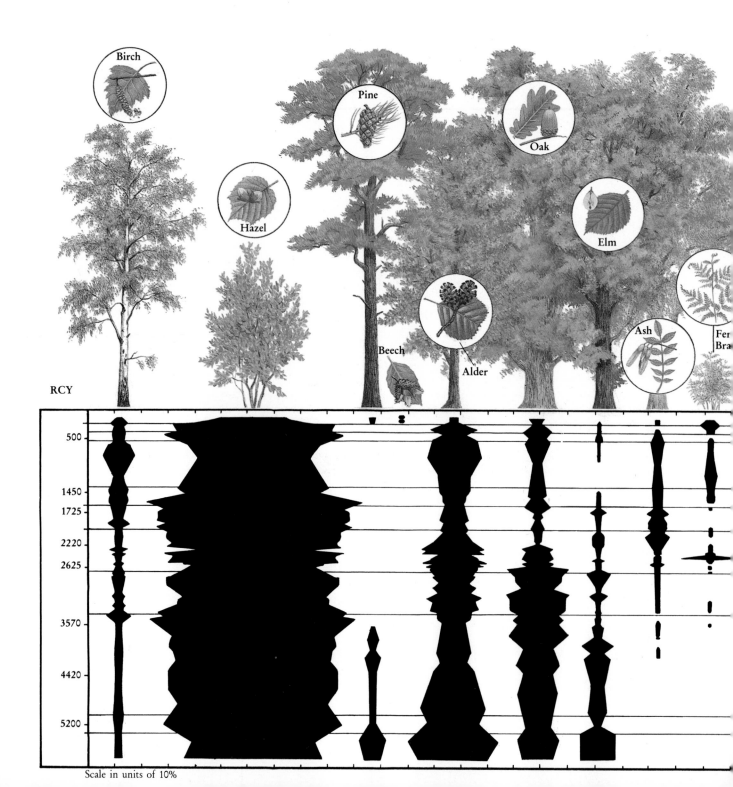

RCY

Birch

Hazel

Pine

Oak

Elm

Beech

Alder

Ash

Fern
Bra

500

1450

1725

2220

2625

3570

4420

5200

Scale in units of 10%

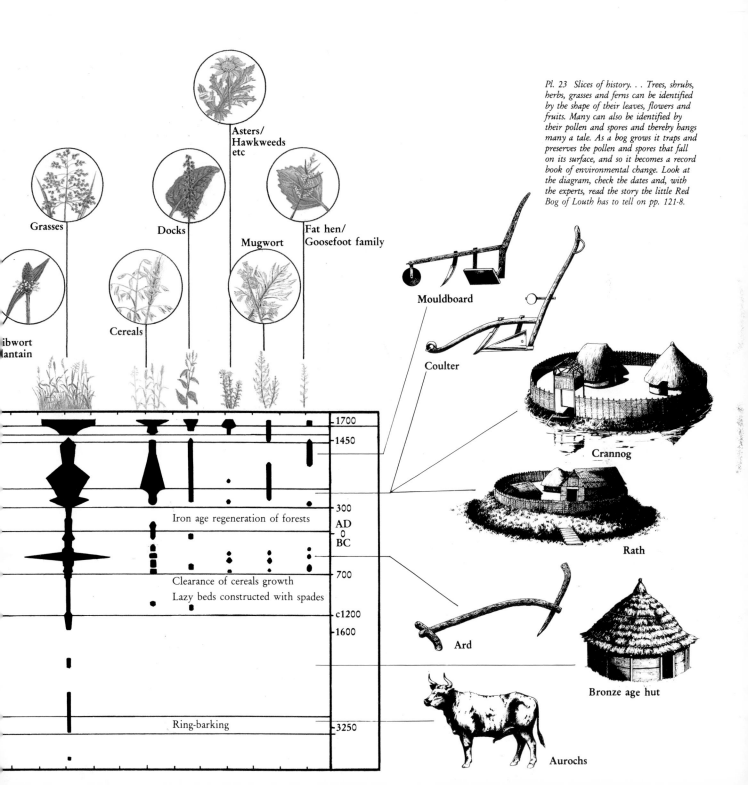

Asters/
Hawkweeds
etc

Grasses

Docks

Mugwort

Fat hen/
Goosefoot family

Cereals

ibwort
lantain

Pl. 23 Slices of history. . . Trees, shrubs, herbs, grasses and ferns can be identified by the shape of their leaves, flowers and fruits. Many can also be identified by their pollen and spores and thereby hangs many a tale. As a bog grows it traps and preserves the pollen and spores that fall on its surface, and so it becomes a record book of environmental change. Look at the diagram, check the dates and, with the experts, read the story the little Red Bog of Louth has to tell on pp. 121-8.

Mouldboard

Coulter

Crannog

Rath

1700

1450

300
AD
0
BC

700

c1200

1600

Iron age regeneration of forests

Clearance of cereals growth

Lazy beds constructed with spades

Ring-barking

3250

Ard

Bronze age hut

Aurochs

BORD FÁILTE

Pl. 24 Stacking the turf to dry is a back-breaking job, which has for centuries brought the reward of warmth all winter from a sweet-smelling fire.

Pl. 25 Ling or heather, a common plant of all boglands. Its young shoots provide food for sheep and grouse alike, and its myriad flowers provide ample nectar for the honey bees. This plant may well hold the world record for pollen production. In a good season one square metre of heather can produce 16,000 million grains — ah-tish-ooo!

Pl. 26 The leafy liverwort Pleurozia purpurea, *with its red-black worm-like strands, is one of the most typical plants of the wetter west, a living signpost, which tells the peatnik exactly where he or she is in Bellamy's Ireland.*

Pl. 27 Head in the cloud berries. . . Cloudberry is a member of the rose flower family and a rare plant of the few mountain blanket bogs. In time the white flower gives way to large succulent though somewhat tasteless berries, called bakeapples in Canada.

HEATHER ANGEL

26

27

28 RICHARD MILLS

29 JOHN FEEHAN

30 GERRY DOYLE

31 J PARNELL

32

SEAN RYAN

Pl. 28   Soft. . . Cotton-grass or bog cottons are common on most of the peatlands. They provide an early bite for all grazing animals in spring and a good show of cottony seeds in the summer. Expert recyclers, they hold onto their minerals year after year.

Pl. 29   . . . and sweet. Sweet gale or bog myrtle, though a typical plant of the western blanket bogs, is only found in soaks on certain raised and ridge-raised bogs. Bacteria living in the roots of the shrub fix nitrogen from the atmosphere, feeding the plant and enriching the peat.

Pl. 30   Transatlantic link. . . Pipewort is one of the special species of pants found in Europe only on the blanket bogs of the west of Ireland and Scotland. Its nearest relatives grow in similar situations in North America.

Pl. 31   Violet or primrose. . .? Water violet, a member of the primrose family, is a rare plant of the early stages of peat formation, and is found only in Antrim and Down.

Pl. 32   Bord na Móna's crock of gold. . . Without rain there could be no rainbows and no bogs. True blanket bogs are only found in areas which in an average year receive more than 1250mm of rain falling on more than 250 days. True raised and ridge-raised bogs like it somewhat drier, for they occur in areas which receive less than 1000mm falling on less than 225 days. Intermediate environments produce intermediate bog types, all part of the great resource which has made Bord na Móna a world-leader in its field.

Pl. 33 Western influence. . . Blanket bog with tussocks of black bog rush and purple moor grass doing its best to live up to its name, blanketing all the land except for the steepest slopes.

Pl. 34 An up and down existence. . . Large tussocks of purple moor grass, a growth form typical of many grasses and sedges that live in habitats with a fluctuating water table.

33

GERRY DOYLE

34

GERRY DOYLE

72

with wave action, will tend to keep them open and even to enlarge the pools.

In certain areas and situations, erosion phenomena are so dominant that a very peculiar form of peat develops. The most extreme I have ever seen is on Achill Island. There, over considerable areas, the whole surface of the bog is broken up into little stools of peat, 25 to 70cm high and about the same distance apart. The only bog moss present in any abundance was *Sphagnum cuspidatum* in the deepest hollows, the most striking addition to the flora being thick mats of blue-green algae, some of which have the ability to fix nitrogen from the atmosphere, enriching the bog with the most soluble of all nutrients, nitrates.

Again, every permutation and combination of these surface features may be found, providing a bewildering diversity to understand and an equally bewildering complexity of hummocks to fall over, and pools to fall into, as you make your way across the bog, your mind on botanical matters.

Plant Life on the Blanket Bog
The plants which go to make up the blanket peats are in the main the same as those whose immortal remains build the domes of the raised bogs. There are, however, some surprises both on the surface and in store in the peat, including some striking omissions and additions to the flora.

For a start, although all species are present, the bog mosses are far less abundant as living cover on the blanket bogs, being usually less than fifty per cent as compared to almost one hundred per cent on the active raised bogs. The bulk of both the rest of the living vegetation and of the peat is made up of sedges and grasses. The only two species found on raised bogs which are generally missing from the blanket peats are bog rosemary and cranberry, although the latter is found, but very rarely.

Special blanket bog plants in order of importance in the peat-forming community

Black bog rush
Purple moor grass
Sweet gale
Many-stemmed spike rush
Bell heather
Bog lousewort
Heath milkwort
Tormentil
Pale butterwort

The species found on lowland blanket but not on raised bogs are more numerous and of great interest. Each one brings its own splash of colour, enlivening the bogland scene at certain times of the year: black, silver purple, red orange, straw yellow, crimson purple, deep pink, gentian blue, bright yellow and pale, pale pink. There is also the added excitement of finding a pure white albino form of any one, for the populations are as diverse as the terrain. Match the colours of the flowers to the list of special blanket bog plants (in the box, p.00) or better still take a trip and see them for yourself — flowers for every season, each one a reason for making a trip to this wild and wonderful land again and again.

Two special plants, one a liverwort, the other a moss, are here in abundance, their special colours and characters greeting you the year round. The crimson-black, worm-like strands of the liverwort *Pleurozia purpurea* enliven the hollows and their margins, while *Camplyopus atrovirens*, a moss, makes its presence felt among the *Sphagna* as it may account for five per cent or more of the living cover. It is a magnificent moss with bright golden silky tips to its leaves, which arise from a jet-black base; perhaps a good common name for it would be the 'spiked punk hair moss'.

Two other groups of plants are special to this region, although whether they can be considered as real members of the bog flora is open to discussion. The first are bog pondweed, pipewort and water lobelia. These abound round the shallow edges of lakes and pools whether they are being colonised or eroded. There, together with many other water-loving plants, they give the bog edge a character all its own. As the process of succession goes on apace, some of these plants become squeezed out, but others appear to be able to remain at least for some time as part of the bog flora. These survivors are bog pondweed, pipewort, common reed and saw sedge and even the white waterlily can be found, much reduced in vigour, marooned in *Sphagnum*-filled hollows.

As we have seen, the bog is a whole mixture of lakes, pools, lawns, hummocks and hollows. As some of these are building and some are eroding, it becomes almost impossible to sort out which plants belong to which facies of development or destruction. This is made even more of a problem when springs and streams bring mineral-rich and mineral-enriched waters to wander their way across the surface of the bog. As a rule of a very wet thumb, it seems safe to say that the true bog surface isolated from any mineral inflow except that of rain may contain all the plants listed, though perhaps some are only of relict status, 'hangers on' from a previous stage of development.

However, any area abounding in the plants shown in the box (p. 75) as fen plants must be regarded as being subject to the effect of mineral-rich or mineral-enriched groundwater, and so they must be classified as fens. (See the box on bog and fen pH, p. 75). It is very tempting to put great tracts of bogland into the category of fens, and as we shall see, anyone coming from Europe without

Plants typical of fens

Common spike rush
Marsh pennywort
Bulbous rush
Blunt-flowered rush
Bulrush
Lesser spearwort
Scorpion moss
Other brown mosses

pH of blanket bog surface	4.0 – 4.8
pH of blanket bog flushes and lakes (fens)	4.3 – 5.52
pH of open pools	5.44 – 6.38
pH of raised bog surface	3.68 – 4.01
pH of raised bog soaks	4.08 – 4.70

All these are means of 1026 recordings made over a period of two days in dry weather in August 1960.

prior knowledge would have ample justification for coming to that conclusion.

The other group of plants which are so special to this area that any visitor would want to see them also abound around the margins of lakes and pools. However, as all can be found growing on peat, they may be regarded as bogland species. These are five members of the heather flower family. St Dabaeoc's heath is widely distributed in western Galway and parts of west Mayo and although it does best straggling up through bushes and shrubs, it is at home rooted in the open peat. The Irish heath has the reverse distribution in the two counties, being more widespread in County Mayo. The third, Mackay's heath, is very rare, being confined to west Donegal and the area of Roundstone in west Galway. Where the latter two grow together, hybrids or something fitting that description have been variously named and argued about in the highest botanical circles, for the original plant has been kept under cultivation at Edinburgh Botanic Garden since its discovery in 1890. The rarest is the Dorset heath found only at one spot near Roundstone.

A fifth member of the group was discovered only in 1936 on a flushed area of blanket bog near Belcoo in County Fermanagh. The plant in question is the Cornish heath, one of the few members of the genus which is tolerant of base-rich conditions. (Other indicators of base-rich conditions found growing in the same habitat were broad-leaved cotton-grass and tawny sedge.) Although somewhat

75

outside the main area of blanket bog, this single site for the Cornish heath in the whole of Ireland is of great interest, one tiny habitat where the conditions are right for its survival as they must have been somewhere in the vicinity, since it reached this place, the furthest north it grows in the natural world.

All these members of the heather flower family are part of what is called the *lusitanian* element of the flora. That is a group of plants which are found only in the wetter west of Ireland and again in western France, Spain, Portugal and some in the western Mediterranean. Three other plants complete the hard core of this assemblage of plants which seems to like it wet and warm. They are the great butterwort found in seepage areas and bogs in Kerry, Cork and Clare; the kidney saxifrage which, though a plant of wet rocks, wanders onto the peat alongside streams in Kerry and West Cork; and the strawberry tree which sheds its pollen into, and casts its shade on, bogs in Kerry, west Cork and Sligo. Botanical interest in these plants centres not only on their presence and their survival, but on how they got there, a question which will be answered by the bogs, as they tell the story of the last 12,000 years of Irish history and more.

Perhaps it is not too surprising to find such warmth-demanding plants tucked away within the area of blanket bog, but those same peatlands also hold some real surprises in plants with a very different origin. The yellow marsh saxifrage, a plant of arctic and sub-arctic Europe, is found in only two locations in Ireland, amongst the bogs around Bellacorrick in County Mayo and in the mountain blanket bogs of Antrim. Likewise, the very rare mosses *Meesia triquetra* and *Homalothecium nitens* have their only Irish stations in tiny flushes within the blanket bogs. These are just some of a group of arctic alpine and montane plants which seem out of place at and around sea level in the warm wet west.

Arctic alpine plants found in the area of blanket bogs

Mountains avens*
Yellow mountain saxifrage
Spring gentian*
Blue moor grass*
Bearberry

*not found on bogs

This group of plants forges a direct and more understandable link with those of the upland and mountain blanket bogs. The flora and upland blankets differs from that of the lowland blankets by the deletion of some plants and by the addition of others. Those missing include pipewort, water lobelia and dwarf juniper. Dwarf juniper does occur in the mountains, but not on deep peat. Black bog rush climbs the hills, but doesn't get very far and is not a true component of the mountain blanket bogs, which include in their floras bilberry and cranberry and, on one or two bogs in the Sperrin Mountains, cloudberry.

The deciduous bilberry (which is better known as the fraughan in Ireland) is of interest because on the southern part of its European range it appears to require shade of bushes and trees and is an important component of bog forest. In the absence of bog forest in Ireland it is found on peat only at altitude on the cool mountain bogs and in one or two spots in shade on the soaks of raised bogs.

Thus we turn full circle to the vexing problem of the actual difference between the raised and the blanket bogs. The only clear distinction between the two main types, raised and blanket, would appear to be that in the true oceanic climate, acid blanket bog peat can begin to grow on leached mineral ground without a buffer zone of fen peat.

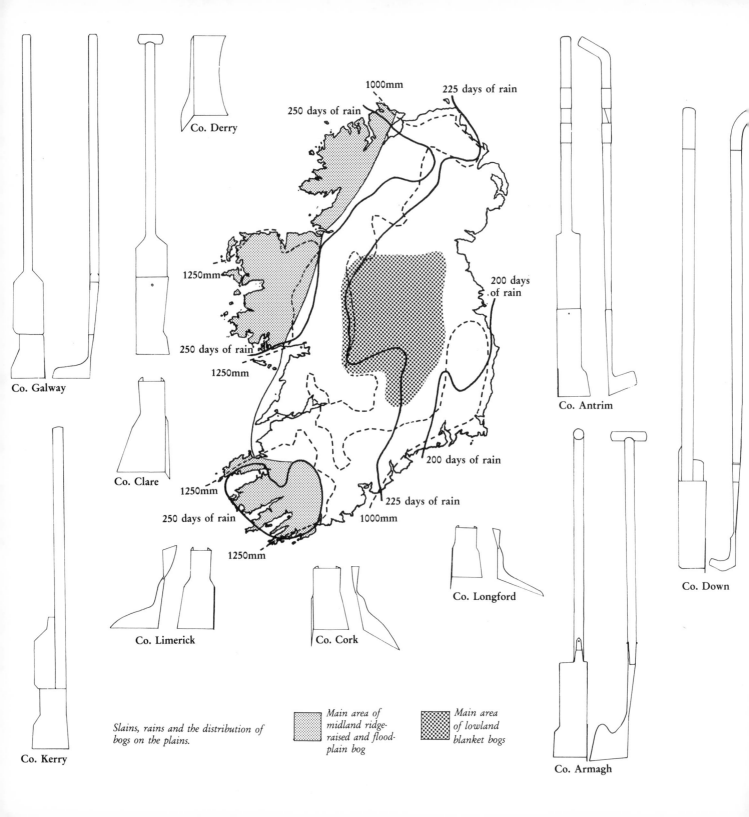

Co. Derry

Co. Galway

Co. Clare

Co. Kerry

Co. Limerick

Co. Cork

Co. Longford

Co. Antrim

Co. Down

Co. Armagh

1000mm

250 days of rain

225 days of rain

1250mm

200 days of rain

250 days of rain

1250mm

200 days of rain

1250mm

250 days of rain

225 days of rain

1000mm

1250mm

Slains, rains and the distribution of bogs on the plains.

Main area of midland ridge-raised and flood-plain bog

Main area of lowland blanket bogs

CHAPTER 4:
SALTS OF THE EARTH

Imagine you are a trained parachutist and you have just landed somewhere in Europe. You would immediately know if you had landed on a bog or fen, for you would be wet and at least your feet would have sunk into peat. On looking around it would not be too difficult to determine that you were on a convex surface, a hump fed only by rainwater, with its own internal drainage system. Armed with the first three chapters of this book, the question would then arise, 'Raised, ridge-raised or blanket?' A question which would at least in part be answered by the common and abundant members of the flora.

If the bog vegetation did not include cross-leaved heath and bog ashpodel, you would probably be somewhere in central Europe. If these two oceanic species were present and the flora of the drainage soak contained sweet gale, another member of the group, then you could say with conviction that you were somewhere close to the Atlantic coast of the continent and probably in Scotland, Wales or Ireland.

Apart from these special oceanic plants, you would also find that many-flowered bog cotton and deer sedge were present on the bog plane. Although all these species are found in abundance on peatlands in central Europe, there they are typically plants of the fens, rarely growing even in soaks. If the bog on which you had landed also contained carnation sedge, brown-beaked sedge and *Sphagnum subsecundum* (all found only as fen plants in more continental climates) on its surface with an abundance of sweet gale and purple moor grass in the soak, you would be right to conclude that you were in the land of suboceanic bogs.

A landing on a true blanket bog, though just as wet, would be much easier to determine. The special highly oceanic and lusitanian plants *Pleurozia purpurea* and pale butterwort would be in evidence and the dominance of the bog mosses, in part usurped by *Campylopus atrovirens* would again place you close to the western seaboard of Europe. The presence of pipewort would narrow it down to western Scotland and Ireland, but the factor which would finally clinch your location as the warm, wet west would be the fenlike character of the whole complex.

79

The abundance of black bog rush (a fen plant throughout the rest of Europe), purple moor grass and sweet gale on the bog plane, with scorpion moss, many-stemmed spike rush, and bog pondweed in soaks is found nowhere else in Europe. These special highly oceanic bog/fens appear to be confined to those lowlands areas of Ireland which receive more than 1250mm of rain, falling on no less than 250 days per year: not only the *amount* of rain, but also the *number* of wet days in the year is important.

Mineral-rich Rainwater
So why are these rain-drenched western Irish bogs so like fens? Partly because they are fed an unusually rich diet of minerals by the rain. But why should the rain have such a high concentration of minerals in areas close to the coast? When seawater evaporates the salts are left behind and water alone passes up to form the clouds and eventually to fall as rain, pure sweet water. The rain may, however, be enriched in a number of ways: natural erosion of the earth's crust producing wind-borne material called *loess*, atmospheric pollution, the destruction of forests and other natural vegetation, aerial irrigation and the spraying of chemicals or use of aerosols. The predominantly westerly winds carry these products of natural and people-produced erosion, enrichment and pollution away from Ireland.

There is, however, another way in which rain becomes charged with minerals. As the wind blows across the open ocean it whips up tiny droplets of seawater and can carry them along for considerable distances. The more stormy the conditions the more seawater will be picked up in this way.

To prove that it does get picked up and that it can be carried onshore, two scientists working at the Freshwater Biological Association in the English lake district studied Ennerdale Water, a lake situated 12 kilometres from the coast at an altitude of 160 metres. Two days of westerly gales, well laced with rain, raised the concentration of sodium in the lake by 0.7 parts per million (ppm). Calculation showed that in order to achieve this increase in concentration, 3000 tonnes of seawater must have been dumped on the catchment. 3000 tonnes is an awful lot of little drops, but it happened, and, given the right conditions, it is happening all the time.

The supply of such minerals to any terrain will thus depend on the amount of rainfall, distance from the coast and the incidence of stormy weather. So the blanket bogs of western Ireland should receive more than their average share.

Now I must confess that the next few pages are a bit complicated. Please don't be put off by all the chemical information. The bogs aren't. In fact it is in part due to these subtle differences in water chemistry that Ireland's bogs are so unique. However, for those who, like me, prefer plants to chemistry, feel free to jump to p. 85).

Chemistry of German Bog Waters

In an attempt to clarify the matter we will look at the water chemistry of peatlands in central Europe, far away from any complications of the coastal environment. The box below gives the mean analytical data of rainwaters collected from the full range of peatland types found in south Germany.

Type
1. 439 ppm Bicarbonate > Calcium > Magnesium > Sulphate > Chloride > Sodium > Potassium   pH 7.6
2. 377 ppm Bicarbonate > Calcium > Sulphate > Magnesium > Chloride > Sodium > Potassium   pH 6.8
3. 139 ppm Bicarbonate > Calcium > Sulphate > Magnesium > Chloride Sodium > Potassium   pH 6.3
4. 61 ppm Sulphate > Bicarbonate > Calcium > Chloride > Magnesium > Potassium > Sodium   pH 5.1
5. 30 ppm Sulphate > Calcium > Chloride > Potassium > Sodium > Magnesium > Bicarbonate   pH 4.2
6. 26 ppm Sulphate > Calcium > Chloride > Potassium > Sodium > Magnesium > Bicarbonate   pH 3.8
7. 19 ppm Sulphate > Chloride > Calcium > Sodium > Potassium > Magnesium > Bicarbonate   pH 3.6
Rain 5 ppm Sulphate > Calcium > Chloride > Sodium > Potassium > Magnesium > Bicarbonate   pH 4.5

The pattern of difference is very striking. Type 1, 2 and 3 peatlands are without doubt under the influence of flowing groundwater rich in minerals, especially bicarbonate and calcium slightly acid to alkaline in reaction. In type 4 the pH falls below 6 and bicarbonate no longer dominates the ionic make-up; however, the effect of flowing groundwater must still be there. These are the lake and fen peats.

Type 5 shows a marked change. In these waters, bicarbonate is relegated to the bottom of the ionic table so it can be inferred that the effect of flowing groundwater is minimal. The ionic make-up of the dilute acid waters approximates to that of the rain, indicating that rain falling directly on the bog and its immediate leached catchment is now a dominant feature of both the water and mineral supply of the poor fens.

In types 6 and 7 the transition is complete, the full acidifying power of the bog mosses is manifest in the low pH and their waters though four times more concentrated than the rain have exactly the same ionic makeup. These are the true bogs.

Chemistry of the Irish Bog Waters

Now, the same is also true of the peatlands in Ireland. The box on p. 82 gives the mean analytical results for water collected from all the main types of peatland in central Ireland — that is water collected from lakes, fens, poor fens and the cupolas of ridge-raised and flood-plain bogs.

Type
1. 277 ppm Bicarbonate > Calcium > Chloride > Sulphate > Sodium > Potassium > Magnesium   pH 7.3
2. 249 ppm Bicarbonate > Calcium > Chloride > Sulphate > Sodium > Magnesium > Potassium   pH 6.9
3. 159 ppm Bicarbonate > Calcium > Chloride > Sodium > Sulphate > Magnesium > Potassium   pH 6.4
4. 64 ppm   Chloride > Bicarbonate > Sodium > Potassium > Sulphate > Calcium > Magesium   pH 5.8
5. 43 ppm   Chloride > Sulphate > Sodium > Bicarbonate > Potassium > Magnesium > Calcium   pH 4.4
6. 30 ppm   Chloride > Sulphate > Sodium > Magnesium Potassium > Calcium > Bicarbonate   pH 4.2
7. 29 ppm   Chloride > Sulphate > Sodium > Magnesium > Calcium Potassium > Bicarbonate   pH 4.0

The differences between the seven main groups closely follow those shown from central Europe, an overall dilution and acidification of the water as rainfall and the bog process takes over dominance from the effects of flowing groundwater. Three main differences are, however, very obvious.

1. *Lower concentration of minerals in the true fen waters.* This can probably be explained by the higher rates of past leaching and the lower rates of contemporary evaporation in the oceanic climate.

2. *Lower acidity of the waters* except those of Stage 1. This could be explained by the greater amount of minerals supplied by the rain or by some other factor.

3. *Importance* and in most cases predominance *of chloride and* to a lesser extent *sodium* in the ionic balance of the water — common salt brought in by rain despite the fact that all the bogs included in the above analysis are from the central plain not from close to the coast.

Chemistry of the Lowland Blanket Bog Waters
Sixty samples of water were collected for analysis from watershed situations within the main blanket bog areas over a period of twenty-four hours in August 1960. The mean result of those analyses is shown with the mean of 100 samples collected from watershed situations in ten ridge-raised bogs for comparison.

Ridge-raised
29 ppm Chloride > Sulphate > Sodium > Magnesium > Calcium > Potassium > Bicarbonate   pH 3.9
Blanket
57 ppm Chloride > Sodium > Sulphate > Magnesium > Bicarbonate > Calcium > Potassium   pH 4.5

The difference is at once clear: the concentration of minerals in the waters of the lowland blanket bogs is almost double that of the ridge-raised bogs, and chloride and sodium are in the 1 and 2 positions, with free bicarbonate present and a pH of 4.5. In comparison with the waters from central Europe their mineral concentration and acidity lie somewhere between stage 4, a fen, and stage 5, a poor fen, reason enough perhaps for the fen-like character of their vegetation, the explanation being simply the increased amount of sea-spray minerals dumped by the rain so close to the coast.

Monmor Bog Squashes a Theory

What a lovely theory! And so it might have remained but for a trip I made to the Kilkee peninsula to look at the remnants of the once great Monmor Bog described by Praeger as 'the centre of an extensive bog district now much reduced by cutting'. Reduced it may be, but there amongst the lakes and pools fringed with pipewort and water lobelia were a number of stretches of what, according to the above theory, should be the perfect example of blanket bog, situated as it is within one kilometre of a very exposed coast, pointing like a finger out into the storm-lashed Atlantic. Imagine the surprise when the vegetation, though of great interest, was devoid of all the markers of true blanket bogs: no black bog rush, no sweet gale, purple moor grass was very rare and, although *Campylopus atrovirens* was present, the full complement of the bog mosses made up for well over fifty per cent of the ground cover. The bog near Kilkee was of an intermediate type whose flora resembled those of the central plain much more than it did those of the western blanket bogs.

Analysis of its waters bore out the supposition, for though the ionic concentration was the highest of all the bogs studied to date, the mean pH of its waters was 4.0 and free dissolved bicarbonate was zero. Further investigation revealed a number of other such intermediate bogs, all of which had floras closely resembling those of the ridge-raised bogs of the central Irish plain, but with some additional 'fen' plants. Mean analysis of the waters of these bogs is given for comparison.

Blanket
57 ppm Chloride > Sodium > Sulphate > Magnesium > Bicarbonate > Calcium > Potassium   pH 4.5

Kilkee
66 ppm Chloride > Sodium > Sulphate > Magnesium > Calcium > Potassium > Bicarbonate   pH 4.0

Castleconnel
40 ppm Chloride > Sodium > Sulphate > Potassium > Magnesium > Calcium > Bicarbonate   pH 4.1

Fallahogy
38 ppm Chloride > Sulphate > Sodium > Magnesium > Potassium > Calcium > Bicarbonate   pH 4.1

Clonbeal
27 ppm Chloride > Sulphate > Sodium > Magnesium > Potassium > Calcium > Bicarbonate   pH 4.0

Ridge-raised
29 ppm Chloride > Sulphate > Sodium > Magnesium > Calcium > Potassium > Bicarbonate   pH 3.9

Apart from the intermediate character of their water chemistry and their vegetation, the only factor apparently linking these intermediate bog types is their climate. They all lie in areas with less than 1250mm of rain falling on less than 250 rain-days per year (which is apparently the lower limit for the true blanket bogs). They are also all in areas with more than 1000mm of rain falling on more than 225 days per average year (which would thus appear to be the upper limit for the formation of the true flora of raised and ridge-raised bogs).

Minerals in Balance

If this is true, and at present it is no more than mere supposition, circumstantial evidence with no proof, then the anomalous fen-like flora of the blanket bogs is not simply due to an excess of rain-borne minerals dumped on the surface of the bog. The explanation must be more complex. The key would appear to be that some overall balance in the ionic composition of the water or some other factor must be reached, some threshold passed allowing the fen plants, and especially the black bog rush, to grow.

Rain falling onto the surface of the land not only brings things with it, but it also carries things away. Leaching is after all the main formative feature of all Irish soils and especially of those of the wet west. Moving water can carry away not only the good things, like minerals, nutrients and bases, but also the acid by-products of the plants which would otherwise collect in the soil. It could well be that the more constant rainfall helps to keep the acidity down and the bicarbonate up to fen level. The question then is, how does this have such a dramatic effect on the flora?

One hypothesis relates to that lightest of all metals, aluminium. Although aluminium is the fourth commonest element in the earth's crust, it is very toxic to most forms of life. Fortunately, over the normal range of pH found on the face of the earth it is insoluble and so remains out of harm's way locked up in the soil or clay or rocks. However, at higher or lower pH values, aluminium dissolves in the form of either aluminate or aluminic ions, both of which are highly toxic. It is suggested that at the pH which prevails in normal bogs, aluminic ions will be present in sufficient quantity to kill off all but the highly tolerant, slow-growing true bog plants.

Another factor which may also be of importance relates to another common element, nitrogen. Without nitrogen there would be no life on earth for it is a vital ingredient of all amino acids and proteins which are the backbone of the living process. Too little nitrogen and nothing can live, let alone grow. It is for this reason that farmers spend vast amounts of money on buying and applying nitrate fertilisers. However, it is equally true that too much nitrogen will cause death, for certain nitrogenous compounds are very toxic. It is for this reason that all higher animals have efficient kidneys to remove excess nitrogen from the system;

84

failure of these vital organs leads to death by toxaemia.

A staggering seventy-eight per cent of the earth's atmosphere consists of nitrogen. Fortunately, pure nitrogen is inert and so cannot by itself enter into chemical reaction; it needs a helping hand. At the other end of the scale, nitrates (nitrogen compounds) are so soluble that they will soon be leached away by the rain or by groundwater flow. It is important to life on earth to maintain an adequate and continuous supply of nitrogen, because, as the adage goes, a little of what you fancy does you good. So it is that simple microscopic organisms, living free in the soil or in symbiotic union within the tissues of more complex plants and animals, are able to activate and 'fix' nitrogen from the air, turning it into nitrate. Likewise, there are other micro-organisms which break down excess nitrate, returning nitrogen to the atmosphere. The one process is called *nitrogen fixation*, the other *dentrification*, and the essence of success is to strike a living balance.

All fens are well supplied with nitrogen fixers. These include free-living organisms, which feed on the products of decay, and symbiotic bacteria, which live in nodules on the roots of members of the pea-flower family, alder and sweet gale. The same is also true for the poor fens, although to a markedly lesser extent. In no case (and more than 1000 tests have been made) has nitrogen fixation been demonstrated in true bog situations; except, that is, in the blanket bogs of western Ireland where sweet gale also grows in abundance.

This sweet-smelling shrub is also often a luxuriant component of the soaks of the ridge-raised bogs. The key pH appears to be 4.5, not too acid. Above this level, nitrogen fixation can take place, and water flow is again implicated, perhaps cleansing the system of excess nitrate, for Kilkee and the other intermediate bogs also toe the line in this respect: sweet gale is absent from their bog planes and their surface peats show negligible amounts of nitrogen fixation, although both occur in soaks and cutaways.

There is one strange anomaly: mountain blanket bogs lack the special fen flora and the nitrogen fixers. Altitude cannot be the only reason for this, for all the fen plants climb higher into the hills in other communities and habitats. Study has shown that the amount of sea salts deposited by wind and rain falls away with altitude, so supply of bicarbonates and minerals could in part be the answer. Also, the lower temperatures in the mountains must affect the rate of activity of the decomposers, slowing decomposition and release of minerals.

Stories to Tell
So it is that even the living skin of the peatlands of Ireland have their own stories to tell, the details of which have not yet been fully unravelled.

Story number one relates to growth and development of plant communities under extreme conditions in which retention and recycling of nutrients is the key to survival. In the future it may be possible to use the genetic information contained within these plants to breed more productive species whch could make such marginal areas of more use to farming.

Story two relates to the nitrate problem. When my original study was made in the late 1950s, all the water samples were analysed for nitrates and none of them was found to contain more than 0.1mg per litre, the limit of accurate detection by the method used. Since that time increasing use of nitrate fertilisers on crops and grassland leys has caused concern across the world, so much so that the World Health Organisation has issued strict guidelines concerning the amount of nitrate allowed in water used for human consumption. The apparently delicate balance of nitrogen fixation on the bogs and fens of Ireland may well be important in understanding and monitoring the overall balance of nitrates in the natural and the human environment.

Story number three concerns the delicate balance of flora in relation to rainfall and acidity which may well be the finger on the pulse of other changes in the European and world environment. In recent years much international concern has arisen over the supposed effect of *acid rain*. The source of the acidity is identified as the burning of fossil fuels. The evidence is conflicting and some authorities argue that the main biological effects for which acid rain is blamed are in fact due to changes in landscape use. Whatever the exact truth of the matter, acid rain is etching its way into the environment. Studies in Ireland indicate a drop in the pH of rain of some 0.4 units over a twenty-year period (1960–79) at the end of which forty-eight per cent of the samples collected had a pH below 5.5 which suggests acidification from an external source. This is a very worrying trend. Ireland does not have much in the way of polluting heavy industry, and with a small population, fuelled at least in part by non-polluting turf, it should be the last to show signs of change, especially as it sits on the edge of the continent in a westerly airstream. If these changes are really taking place on a massive enough scale, the results should soon be evidenced by changes in the flora of the bogs.

The living skin of Ireland's unique peatlands are the final finger on the pulse of change in the environment of Europe. The only trouble is that by the time these environmental changes affect our boglands it may be too late to do anything about changing this particular course of history. Whatever happens, we can only hope that some of the bogs and fens will still be there to take down the evidence as they have done since Ireland was covered not by peat and soil but by water frozen solid by the last ice age.

CHAPTER 5:
TAKING DOWN THE EVIDENCE

The evidence faithfully recorded in subfossil form by the growing peat is intricate in the detail not only of what has occurred on that spot throughout time but also of what has occurred in the environs of the bog or fen. The evidence comes in all shapes and sizes from tree stumps and trunks, great antlers and bones, down to the minutest pollen grains and spores.

The Giant Deer
Without doubt the most famous subfossils to be found in Ireland are the remains of the giant deer with the magnificent Latin name of *Megaloceros giganteus*. Two metres to the shoulder, the male of the species stood resplendent with a set of antlers spanning almost three metres — a majestic sight. Spectacular they must have been, but when it came to battle they were of little use, for in order to keep their weight down to manageable proportions, strength was entirely lacking.

Perhaps the most fantastic and certainly the most limiting aspect of owning these gigantic bony structures was that they were shed and had to be regrown anew each year — an amazing feat which would have required good supplies of both food and minerals, especially calcium, in the spring of the year when supplies of fodder where not at their best. Using all the modern sophistications of science, the remains of Ireland's giant deer have in the main been dated to between 13,000 and 11,000 years ago. Most of the skeletons and antlers have also been found in lake muds rich in the remains of shells which were sealed over, first by clays and sands and later by peat. The scenario of the death of these animals is simple to imagine: they came down to browse on the rich fen and lakeside vegetation, and, unbalanced by their unwieldy antlers, they toppled and got caught by the weeds which became both their shroud and their coffin.

In order to understand what vegetation provided these monarchs of the glens of Ireland, the Isle of Man and, to a lesser extent, Britain with the food and the calcium they needed for annual growth, we need only turn to the smallest of the subfossils in the peaty record book.

The Pollen Evidence

Like bones and antlers, wood is a structural feature with inbuilt strength and so it is likely to survive the ravages of decomposition and time. However, many smaller organisms have need of protection throughout their lifetime, however short, and so survive well also in subfossil form. The external skeleton of insects is a prime example as are the pollen grains and spores of plants. The only problem is to find them in the peaty matrix, get them out into view and then give them a name.

Pollen grains of flower- and cone-bearing plants and the spores of ferns, club-mosses, horse-tails, mosses, liverworts and fungi are wrapped in *sporopollenin*, a chemical which is so resistant to decay that it can be found in the oldest sedimentary rocks. What is more, in many cases the protective wall is textured and sculptured into intricate patterns, which in some cases are instantly recognisable by the expert, who can tell which sort of plant produced the spores or grains. So it comes about that any peat deposit contains a sample of the spores and pollen grains which fell on its surface every year throughout its build-up, a detailed record of the plants which grew on its surface and in its vicinity.

The name of this game is *pollen analysis* and it is played by collecting peat samples from known depths. Using strong chemicals the humified peat is dissolved away leaving the tough grains and spores which, after concentration in a sort of scientific spin dryer called a centrifuge, are stained, identified and counted. Pollen analysis of the lake and peat deposits found below, around and above the giant antlers provides us with the following story.

Ice Ages and Warm Spells (15,000 years ago)

Fifteen thousand years ago there was little pollen of any sort blowing about anywhere in Ireland, for, like the rest of the continent of Europe to which it was then joined, Ireland was just emerging from beneath the ice sheets of a glacial epoch which had in all lasted for much more than a million years. That doesn't mean that the whole of Ireland had been covered by ice for that long — far from it. Even during the last two hundred thousand years the temperature had fluctuated up and down on at least nine occasions and ice sheets had waxed and waned at least twice.

The development of large ice masses has three major effects. In the first place, they lower the level of the sea, because a good deal of the sea's water goes to form the snow and ice; secondly, their weight depresses the surface of the land; and we'll come to the third effect later. As the lowering of sea level is always greater than the depression of the land, islands like Ireland and Britain became joined to each other and to the local continent by impermanent walkways. This was very convenient for those living things like giant deer which can migrate on foot, for as the climate gets bad and the glaciers form, they were able to move south for the long winter, their great-great . . . great-grandchildren returning once more when the weather warmed up. The plants, poor things, just stayed put to be killed by the frost and covered by the ice. They could only make their comeback by hitching a ride on passing animals and birds or being carried on wind, wave and water.

Thanks to the record in the peat and the clays, we know that giant deer were present in Ireland during a warm spell about 30,000 years ago. They then went south, returning 17,000 years later to graze the rich meadows which had developed in the wake of the melting ice, especially in those areas of Ireland now famous as centres of milk production, Limerick, Down and Meath.

Thanks to the pollen record we know that the giant deer fed on lots of lush grasses, well laced with arctic alpine plants, sedges, juicy docks and sorrels and the leaves from small willows and juniper. We also know that there were no, or at least not many, large trees, except perhaps a few scattered stands of birch. This was ideal for giant deer, whose proudest possession made life in forested land almost impossible.

All these plants must have arrived before the deer. Many have light seeds and could be carried on the wind, others were brought in by faster-moving birds and smaller mammals like lemmings, fox, reindeer and hare. All of these we know were there, thanks to the preservative power of the peat, which itself could only begin to form once the right plants had arrived on the wettest parts of the scene.

The third major effect of an ice age is to restructure, remineralise and so rejuvenate the land, ready for plants to grow, animals to graze and leaching to begin. Most of the soils which now bear the richest crops were restructured during — or have been formed anew since — the last glaciation and so have only been open to the ravages of leaching and of the living process for at the most 14,000 years.

Back in those refreshed late glacial times, the beasts fed well, recharged their own internal chemistry and grew a new set of antlers each year larger than the last until some toppled to death and preservation amongst the fen plants which had formed their last supper. For perhaps 2000 years they reigned supreme, and we can only guess how common they were across the length and breadth of their green and grassy land.

But colder weather was now on the way again, grass gave way to sedge and mugwort spread its presence and its pollen across the landscape, as snow patches on the mountains enlarged and became more permanent. The giant deer migrated south-east to warmer climes where they became extinct, trapped perhaps between dense forests to the south and a concentration of predators, including humans, also escaping or held back by this sting in the ice age tail.

During the new cold snap, which lasted but five hundred years, the newly formed and forming soils were opened up once more to the action of deep frost. Cycles of freeze and thaw eroded material down to cover and seal the lake deposits in which the deer had died.

In places the sub-soil probably remained frozen throughout each 'arctic' summer, only the surface melting to form what is known as an 'active layer'. It was into this that crowberry, mountain avens, mountain sorrel, spring gentian and yellow mountain, purple and yellow marsh saxifrage and other arctic alpine plants grew. Though the pollens of most of these plants are difficult — and some impossible — to identify, we know they must have been there, for *relict* populations are still found on the cold mountain tops, cliffs and in special spots amongst those blanket bogs.

The roots of these hardy plants must have done their level best to stabilise the soil, but the constant freeze and thaw pushed ice wedges down into the rock rubble and pulled at the stones, sorting them and the gravels and silts into circles, heaps, polygons and stripes. All this, of course, had happened before on the margin of the main ice sheets as they had melted away 5000 years before. The ice-worked patterns and deposits may still be seen below the peat, telling us that it was very cold. The giant deer, sensible creature that it was, left Ireland as arctic plants spread out from their mountain retreats, and beetles like *Diacheila arctica* and *Amara alpina* — their natural habitat revealed by their second names — flew in upon the scene and left their remains behind as evidence of their fleeting presence.

A Warmer Climate and New Arrivals

From 10,000 years ago the climate took a turn for the better and as the temperature improved, plants and animals returned to Ireland in wave after wave of immigration and peatlands began their growth, taking down the evidence layer by soggy layer.

Trees came in this order, each to dominate and then take a lesser place in the landscape: willow, juniper, birch and hazel.

Pine soon joined the invaders, the tall evergreen trees in places shading out the birch and hazel, their roots reaching down and tapping the rich supplies of minerals. Together these three trees dominated the landscape for more than a millennium. Elm and oak were there, but only later did they usurp the rule of pine.

Stone Age People — The First Inhabitants

By the time the first human colonists set up their camps in Ireland all the native trees, including yew, alder and ash were doing well. Archaeological evidence tells us that the mesolithic (middle stone age) people, who were here between 8700 and 8600 years ago, were hunter-gatherers who used small flint chips (microliths) to give a cutting edge to their hunting implements and the tools with which they butchered meat and prepared their food. Like most hunter-gatherers they made use of everything the environment had to offer and which they had the technology to handle. Many lived in choice coastal sites where the sea provided all sorts of collectables from shellfish to birds' eggs, and the shells and bones preserved in their middens (rubbish dumps) show that birds, fish and mammals all had their place in an enormously varied diet.

The recent find of a mesolithic camp at Lough Boora in central Ireland is of great interest. There as the lake was drained prior to exploitation of the peat from the bogs round about this fascinating site came to light. No foundations of huts were found but hearths and the remains of food, red deer, pig, duck, small birds, fish and hazel nuts were present in abundance. The raw material from which their many implements had been made was chert, itself in plentiful supply along the edge of the lake.

These people who made their implements and cooked their food upon this spot must have seen and traversed the Bog of Allen in its early fen base stage (see pl. 41, p. 102). One can only marvel as to how they made their way across the country, the bulk of which was swathed with woodland, the like of which we cannot see today in Ireland.

Pine, hazel, elm and oak dominated the Irish scene for well over 1000 years, during which time new human settlers came and began to make themselves at home. The Larnian people, who had a greater range of flint implements, moved along the coast and along rivers and about lakes, hunting, fishing and gathering as they went, clearing small areas of trees around their camps, leading what seems to us an idyllic life during this 'climatic optimum', when the average temperature was some 5°C warmer than it is today.

A Wetter Climate (7000 years ago)

Around 7000 years ago the climate appears to have got wetter or at least more oceanic, as alder pollen increased, mainly at the expense of pine and hazel, although the latter soon recovered. Pine, pushed onto the higher, drier ground, could not compete with the broadleaf trees whose roots penetrated deeper for the minerals they then put into cycle. 3000 years of formation must have seen not only the development of structured forest soils but also the leaching of the upper layers, a prelude of what would come once the trees had been cut away. The lushest lowland woodlands now were made up of alder, oak and elm and they must have stretched for hectare upon hectare as they did across the centuries for almost 1500 years. Great trees must have grown to maturity and beyond into the magnificence of old age, their remains rotting when they fell to feed and nurture the next generation of forest giants.

The increased wetness of the climate revitalised the process of peat formation. The fens and fen forests began to expand and the raised bog domes began to grow, taking down more detailed evidence in their acid mor (humus).

The First Farmers (5000 years ago)

About 5000 years ago, the peatland history books record a marked drop in the amount of elm pollen reaching their surface and the record is the same in bogs clear across Europe. At the same time the pollen of pine, alder and oak showed a similar though less dramatic decline, and that of hazel and birch increased. The appearance of the pollen of grasses of broad-leaved plantain and other herbs, dock and nettle rising to weed proportions, together with the discovery of new more sophisticated artefacts suggest the first agricultural revolution and the advent of the neolithic (new stone age) culture. Bands of people, armed with implements of polished stone and with knowledge of animal husbandry, of crop tillage and of ring-barking of trees, must have exploded across Europe and into Ireland. They fed their animals on leaves, especially of the nutrient-rich elm, stripped from the trees, then ring-barked them to kill the canopy, so letting the sunlight onto the grass and perhaps onto their crops, which they planted amongst the dead tree trunks. The massive decrease in elm pollen could also be explained by a Europe-wide epidemic of a disease of the elm tree such as is occurring today. This is a subject of heated argument in scientific circles. But the facts are clear: the elm disappeared and neolithic people came in force upon the scene.

The soils were now opened up to the full leaching power of the rain. The minerals in the soils in each small plot were soon exhausted and so the neolithic farmers moved on to destroy more forest, graze more grass, leaving their earlier plots to regenerate until eventually they disappeared under secondary forest in which state they could be attacked once more, initiating a new cycle of destruction and regeneration.

We know from the complex graves and cemeteries they left behind them that the neolithic people must have had a highly sophisticated economy. The bounty of just twenty square miles of the valley of the River Boyne spared at least a million people-hours over, say, four years to construct the impressive passage grave complex at Newgrange, so it is little wonder that they were able to destroy more and more forest.

We do know that throughout the neolithic period, the peatland scene was changing. Many of the fens which had filled basin sites from saddles through kettle holes to lakes and flood plains were already under fen woodland. They began to expand both outwards and upwards, preparing the way for the development of poor fen and acid bog. To account for this we must invoke some fact or factors which increased the wetness of the surface of the terrain. Climatic deterioration, wetter and/or cooler, could do the trick, but so could the removal (by ring-barking) of the power of the trees to draw water from the landscape and lose it to the atmosphere by evapotranspiration.

Whichever was the actual cause, and I like to think that it was a bit of both, the expanding fens and developing bogs of the lowlands and especially around the fertile lakes and rivers of the central plain must have been of little interest to these stone-age farmers except as a source of game. It must, however, be put

92

on record, as it is in the peat, that the neolithic people appeared to make minimal use of venison. Could it be that the wet, impenetrable fen woodland with their unproductive bog centres were places of awe, or at least no-go areas for their valuable cattle?

Of all the plant communities in the world, fen woodland is about the most difficult to traverse. Though squishy, the open bog surface is easy so long as you know where not to put your feet. Fluffy yellow *Sphagnum cuspidatum,* white-beaked sedge and long-leaved sundew mark the danger spots and can be avoided, because at least you can see where you are going in the open bog. In fen woodland it is impossible – a tangle of partly fallen trunks and branches with dense stands of the dreaded saw sedge and other massive cut-edge plants hide pitfalls and old root-holes full of black, cloying, silty peat. They are places best avoided and up to this time they had, at least in part, been avoided by the neolithic farmers, sensible people that they were. They had headed instead towards the more open forests and better drained forest soils on the hills, leaving the bogs intact to record their progress.

Peat Formation

Whether the weather had deteriorated or not, the effect of neolithic agriculture on these woodland soils, which had been at the most 4000 years in the making, was catastrophic. Crops, however small, took away key minerals, which until then had been held tight in cycle. At the same time, rain began to leach minerals down through the readily draining soil, feeding the fens downslope and in time producing impoverished soil complete with impervious iron pan. The end was near, the forest soil was gone, replaced by podsols (see p. 59) which could no longer support the growth of trees. Water loss from the surface was thus reduced, water could no longer drain away and so the upper layers of the soil became saturated and peat began to form. The first peat was formed of rushes and sedges, their thick perennial parts still further impeding drainage, spreading the effect of podsolisation and paving the way for the bog mosses and for blanket peat.

The one-way process – forest soil, peaty podsol, blanket peat — can be seen again and again wherever excavations have been made through the peat into the soil beneath. It has happened on an enormous scale and across the whole range of rock types from the softest chalks of Antrim to the hardest quartzites of the Twelve Bens in Galway. The only differences being the date of initiation and the type of vegetation which first formed on the peaty podsol, both being partly determined by the base and mineral content of the parent rock.

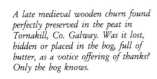

A late medieval wooden churn found perfectly preserved in the peat in Tornakill, Co. Galway. Was it lost, hidden or placed in the bog, full of butter, as a votice offering of thanks? Only the bog knows.

CHAPTER 6:
EVIDENCE FROM UNDER THE BLANKET

On turning up the various accounts of recent archaeological endeavours in the west of Ireland, one is tempted to conclude that wherever the blanket of peat is lifted up, evidence of pre-peat farming may be found.

Please, please, one word of caution: excavation of the heritage of Ireland (and of the world) is the job of experts. Amateurs, however well-meaning, unless directed properly can destroy much more than they can discover. Mere treasure hunters will be disappointed ninety-nine or more times out of a hundred, but the damage their self-seeking endeavours causes is irreparable. The great majority of archaeological finds are piles of stones and bits of charcoal of little monetary value, but if studied in their context they are of immense value to an understanding of ourselves. The blanket bog has preserved them *in situ* untouched for so long and excavation is the work of patient experts.

Pre-bog Farming
Removal of the peat has revealed not only houses of the neolithic dead, but, radiating out from the nomumental tombs, extensive enclosures of earth and stone divided into smaller 'fields' with hut circles and other signs of occupation. On the basis of such exciting discoveries, Seamus Caulfield on the top of the cliffs of Behy Glenulra west of Ballycastle in County Mayo uncovers the following scenario of pre-bog farming (see diagram p. 96):

These conclusions are indicated by the size and layout of the fields. 1) The overall layout has a unity which indicates it was planned and organised as a single decision, whether this was taken by one controlling individual or by communal agreement is not known. 2) The height of the walls indicates that they are functional barriers capable of retaining cattle but not of retaining or excluding sheep and deer. 3) The size of the fields indicates that they were primarily organised for a grass crop. Animal husbandry is therefore likely to have been the inspiration for the Behy/Glenulra field system.

If woodland had regenerated on that spot again, much of this unique information

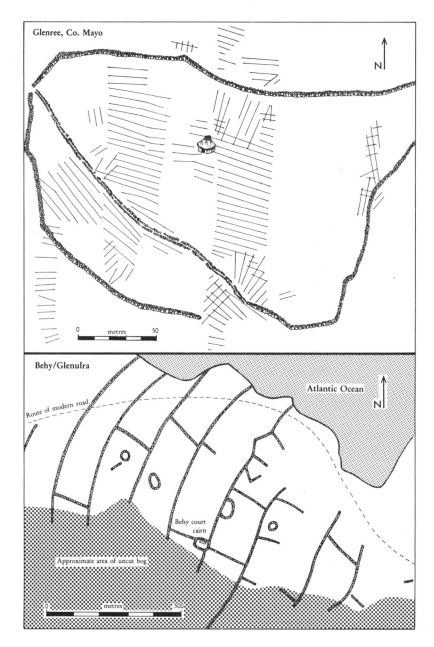

Pl. 35 No less than 300,000 hectares of the wettest tracts of the lowlands are covered with true blanket bog. It is a unique living system found nowhere else on earth, part of the magic of Ireland and preserving so much of its histories. Much of it is of world heritage status and it must be conserved for all our futures.

Evidence from under the blanket — pre-bog farms in County Mayo. At Behy/Glenulra the field systems were used by farmers to graze cattle in neolithic times. The bounty of the fields allowed them time to build the court cairn. At Glenree bronze age farmers made cultivation ridges both within and outside the enclosure walls. Why were some dug at right angles to others and why did the farmers move out and the bog move in? The answer lies hidden in the peat.

Glenree, Co. Mayo

0 metres 50

Behy/Glenulra

Atlantic Ocean

Route of modern road

Behy court cairn

Approximate area of uncut bog

0 metres 500

37

Pl. 36 Lagopus scotius hibernicus. *A male Irish red grouse surveys his territory from a vantage point on an upturned sod of turf. Sweet vernal grass in the foreground shows that the area has been disturbed by drainage and either burning or fertilisation. One can only wonder what will happen to this rare endemic subspecies of game-bird as more of its habitat goes the same way.*

Pl. 37 Bogwood — *forests of the past revealed by the removal of the peat. Much of that part of Ireland now covered with blanket bog once supported mixed forest. Cleared first by neolithic farmers, the soils became so leached by increasing rainfall that they could no longer support the trees. The farmers moved on and the bog plants took over.*

Pl. 38 *Ireland has only two native amphibians — the natterjack toad and the smooth newt. All the rest didn't manage to cross over before the Irish sea filled up after the last ice age. The common frog was introduced in the 1720s and is doing well in callows and cutaways.*

RICHARD MILLS

38

RICHARD MILLS

Pl. 39 Half a wisp. . . If you see more than one then it is a wisp of snipe. A still common bird of marsh, callow and bog. When disturbed, they fly away in zigzag fashion, making a very difficult target. They often dive from the sky making a peculiar drumming noise with their tails.

Pl. 40 Circus cyaneus. Hen harrier with chicks. These birds of prey hunt while flying low over bogs, heaths, swamps and marshes. No wonder they are so at home in Ireland! They build their nests and raise their families on the ground. Hasn't she done well!

RICHARD MILLS

*Pl. 41 A 10,000-year calendar for
County Offaly*

a *Late glacial times: Lakes were fed by
waters flowing to the Shannon, giant
deer browsed on the rich waterside
vegetation, the hills were covered with
arctic tundra.*

b *Stone age times: The first Offaly people
camped around the lakes which were
rapidly filling with peat and, along with
bear, wolf and reindeer, saw the great
Bog of Allen start to grow.*

41

Broad-leaved pondweed
Potamogeton natans

Giant deer
Megaloceros giganteus

Yellow water-lily
Nuphar lutea

Reindeer
Rangifer tarandus

Crowberry
Empetrum nigrum

Bottle sedge
Carex rostranta

Reindeer moss
Cladonia rangiferina

102

Hazel
Corylus avellana

Willow
Salix sp.

Bulrush
Typha latifolia

Wolves
Canis lupus

Cave bear
Ursus spelaeus

Neolithic times: The first farmers on
central Irish plain cleared trees,
[gra]zed their cattle and began the long
[str]uggle of life among the bogs.

d Early Christian times: The giant
cupolas of the Bog of Allen provided a
resting place for white-fronted geese from
Greenland. Perhaps it was these birds

who sowed the seeds of the Rannoch rush
on the Pollagh Bog.

Elm
Ulmus sp.

Oak
Quercus sp.

Scots pine
Pinus sylvestris

Aurochs
Bos primigenius

Greenland white-fronted geese
Anser albifrons flavirostris

*Sphagnum
magellanicum*

Cladium mariscus

Fat hen
Chenopodium album

Corn sowthistle
Sonchus arvensis

Ragwort
Senecio jacobaea

Ribwort plantain
Plantago lanceolata

103

DAVID GREENE

43

Pl. 42 Chilly outlook. . . Turf stacked to dry on upland blanket bog in the background. This wintry scene is chilly enough, but without the promise of the peat an Irish winter would be a much colder experience. By 2030 most of this resource of warmth will be gone.

Pl. 43 Stripped pine. . . The stumps of an ancient pine uncovered when the turf was stripped way. The tree grew on that same spot some 4000 years ago and is rooted in peat which formed when the original mixed forest was cut down by the first farmers.

Pl. 44 Box and all. . . A perfectly preserved gold bracelet with its original wooden container found about 1830 at Killymoon, Co. Tyrone. It dates from about 700 BC.

Pl. 45 Jewelled silver paten and its stand found at the monastic site at Derrynaflan, Co. Tipperary, which was situated on an island surrounded by bog.

Pl. 46 Splendid silver chalice with gold and amber settings found in 1980 with other objects at Derrynaflan, Co. Tipperary. It dates to the ninth century.

44

45

Pl. 47 Hoarding. . . Hoards of gold and bronze tell of the wealth of the people who lived by the bog which preserved their treasures for posterity. A pair of gold armlets from the middle bronze age found in a bog at Derrinboy, Co. Offaly. Below: A riveted bronze cauldron from the late bronze age found near Castlederg, Co. Tyrone.

would have been obliterated. Likewise, if the bog had not grown sealing the site, preserving much of the organic rottable material and making it of little use for future, more sophisticated farming, walls would have been broken, the tombs and huts robbed of their best stone, the information scattered and lost. The bog has preserved it all, in wonderful and intricate detail.

Based on evidence of the size and shape of the fields and of the cattle bones found beneath the peat Seamus Caulfield goes on to hypothesise:

A three-year-old animal, weighing an average 500kg can be taken annually from three hectares. With a sixty per cent killing out rate this represents a 400kg carcass. Each hectare will thus yield 100kg of beef. On these calculations a family farm of circa 25 hectares would be viable and the Behy fields could have supported four or five familes on a beef economy alone.

Even today the farmers of north Mayo can count themselves lucky with a growing season in excess of nine months, the soil temperature of the other three being below the somehow magic 6°C which allows the grass to grow. If, as we believe, the average annual temperature of 5000 years ago was 2°C warmer than it is today, then in north Mayo and other equally favoured parts of the far west the grass may have grown all year round. Lucky farmers indeed, so why did they move out and the bog move in? The answer must lie at least in part in leaching and the development of acidity.

The widespread activity of the neolithic farmers had replaced the protective and recycling powers of natural forest with grassland whose close-knit sward continued the process as best it could, providing recycling protection the year around. Anything which tipped that delicate balance opening up the soil still more to the erosive and leaching power of the rain could have led to catastrophic change. Overgrazing alone could have done the trick, although cooler wetter weather could have helped shift the critical balance destroying the fertility of the soil.

And so, the neolithic farmers did the only thing they could, they moved out and the bog moved in to put its seal of approval on an impoverished acid landscape and to seal in the evidence of change in land use. A record of that period of time between 5000 and 4000 years ago when the husbanding of animals within the shelter of ring-barked trees developed in certain well-endowed places to more intensive operations within drystone walls. The role of trees in this new farming economy was thus relegated to a supply of timber for the construction of houses, for fencing, for cooking food and for keeping warm should the January temperature be mean enough to fall below that which kept the grasses green and growing.

The evidence uncovered to date tells us that over considerable areas of Connacht and northern Mayo the picture was the same. The soils were under grass and some of the farmers, without the restrictions of meat or milk quotas, were doing their best to tame the best bits of the landscape. It also shows that considerable areas had not been turned over to this type of agriculture for there is no evidence of sub-bog walls or fences. These are in the main low-lying sites in which the development of fens and bogs may have been well advanced at the time the neolithic farmers came on the scene. However, so perfect is the record in places that the following stories can be told and statements can be made with conviction.

Pine stumps have been found standing where they grew 7000 years ago when the temperature was even warmer than it was in neolithic climes. Their excellent state of preservation indicates that they must have been quickly taken within the aegis of the anaerobic zone of developing bogs so even during the period of maximum forest cover the balance towards peat formation must have been close and tipped in places.

Belderg Beg on the Coast of North Mayo
At this site neolithic walls, pottery and implements have been found both on the surface and within the upper profile of the mineral soil sealed over with a thin layer of peat which must have begun to grow around 5000 years ago. The farmers had moved out after an occupation of perhaps a few centuries, the peat began to grow and eventually forest moved back in. Stumps of both pine and oak dating from around 4000 years ago have been found preserved where they died, growing on a thin layer of peat, their roots not penetrating into the soil below. Thus it would seem that even at this late stage the ravages wrought by farming could, given time, be healed and the site could once more support the growth of trees as woodland moved back to engulf the landscape.

Some 1500 years after the first farmers left, new ones came to re-colonise the farmland, adding new enclosures and a circular building some 10m in diameter. The building stood on mineral soil, one new wall radiated out across the peat which at that time had a maximum depth of 30cm. The wall petered out to a line of pointed oak stakes which had been driven through the bog to touch the mineral soil beneath. Two of the posts gave almost identical dates 3220 ± 85 and 3210 ± 85 years before present. The building yielded a number of saddle querns and rubbers, stone implements for grinding the grains of cereals. As no other artefacts were found, it was probably a storehouse or granary which was perhaps burned down 3170 years ago, for a block of charcoal found within its walls yielded that date.

Seamus Caulfield wonders why the second lot of farmers used this site and speculates on the supposition that a part peat, part pine-covered landscape would have little to tempt the later farming family to put down roots. That is, unless they had some special reason for selecting the site. Caulfield draws attention to a vein of copper-bearing ore a mile from the site at Belderg Beg which has yielded this fascinating slice of history, a slice which terminates with this brief occupation by bronze age people hungry not only for food but for the raw materials of their new technology. They came, they went and the bog finally closed in, putting paid to farming on the site for at least 3000 years and overlaying the evidence with a lobe of the most extensive history book in Europe.

It is also fascinating to recall that it was modern farmers who make their living in much the same way as their neolithic forebears who began to uncover this wealth of hidden information. The twentieth-century farmers of north Mayo raise cattle and crops and take a rich harvest from the rivers, lakes and sea. The only difference is the implements they use and that, in the absence of wood in a treeless landscape, they cut peat to fuel their hearths. That is how the hidden evidence first came to light.

It was one such farmer, by the name of Tommy Toler, who lives on the Mayo–Sligo border, who, when in need of stones to build the foundations of his house, turned, as many others have done, to the heaps exposed in the local cutaway. There in the base of one of the sub-bog walls he found a flint implement which because of its shape is known as a slug knife and because of its workmanship is dated to the early bronze age. Having seen similar things in the National Museum at Dublin and knowing no others had been found in his vicinity, Tommy reported his find to the museum and sent the knife along to prove it. Subsequent excavations directed by Michael Herity revealed a kidney-shaped enclosure about 150m long by 100m wide. Within the walls were the remains of a circular hut with a central hearth complete with charcoal. Charcoal from another hearth underlying the enclosing wall dated to 3245 ± 85 years before present.

However, the most exciting discovery was that most of the area within the enclosure and for a considerable distance outside the mineral soil bore the distinctive marks of cultivation ridges. These had probably been made using a spade as each averaged about 150cm across. A crop would be sown on top of the ridge on each side of which was a 'furrow' which greatly aided drainage (and leaching). The current landowner was able to demonstrate their method of construction using a long-handled spade the like of which can still be bought at the local farm supply shop.

In one area within the enclosure two sets of ridges were found set at right angles to each other. The later set were designed with back-breaking effort to bring fresh soil to the surface from new *siochs* or 'furrows', though they were not made by ploughs. Even in the absence of the plough, the pollen held within the soil shows that cereals had been planted on the ridges. In other areas the pollen of corn spurrey, a weed of impoverished soils, was present in abundance. Could it be that the soils were becoming impoverished despite the fact that they were digging deeper in a vain search for those leached minerals? Oh for another ice age! Another ice age didn't come and blanket peat became established there about 2600 years ago since which time it has grown some three metres thick, a slab of living history whose record will take us up to the present time.

Agriculture Speeds Peat Initiation

In many places agriculture must have helped to tip the mineral balance, speeding soil impoverishment and eventually peat development on its way. Bronze age technology simply made the processes of agriculture easier to accomplish, as did iron when it arrived on the Irish scene around 2500 years ago, a hundred years after peat started to form on what now is part of Tommy Toler's farm.

Backtracking a little, it must be put on record that further from the warm wet west coast, developing bogs had been getting in the way of farming endeavours as early as 3390 years ago. Trackways made of logs dated to this time have been found laid across bogs in a number of strategic places. The study of similar corduroy tracks found in bogs in other parts of Europe have always been linked with an increased wetness of the bog surface, a speeding of peat growth linked probably to a change in climate. Again it must be emphasised that an increase in peat growth need not necessarily be due to climatic deterioration. Removal of the trees from the catchment of the bog could tip the balance and development time alone could be enough, for once any bog has reached a sufficient size, its own volume begins to be large enough to hold its own water and hence speed its upward and outward growth.

Much more evidence is needed, but there is probably sufficient even now to conclude that about 4000 years ago the pace of peat growth was changing out of bottom gear clear across the country. Whatever the actual cause, it was just in time to take down the evidence of successive technologies which changed the pace and the face of both farming and of pollen falling on the surface of the developing bogs.

Buried by the Bog

One such bog has been investigated both in depth and in the detail it deserves: Red Bog in County Louth. Its layered 100 per cent pure organic history book gives a clear picture of the changes wrought by 5000 years of technological development all supported by the richness of those post-glacial soils or at least what remained beyond the reach of the peat and the leaching power of the rain. However, before turning those particular wet pages of history engrained with ordered knowledge, a tale of mystery and treasure trove.

If the blanket of peat can cover and preserve such a wealth of information relating to pre-bog cultures, it stands to reason that as the peat grows it will swallow up and preserve most artefacts which fall or are placed within its mor. When winning turf it is thus always a source of wonder or worry as to exactly what the next stroke of the slain may reveal; for such finds range from bog gold to bog bodies.

Bog Hoards

Bog hoards are groups of artefacts found together where they were either laid or lost in the bog or in a place that eventually became covered by peat. Whether the artefacts are ornamental or utilitarian or made of noble or base metal, stone, wood fibre or cloth, their value is immense, for they give us an insight into past cultures and customs.

How or why each of the hoards got to its peaty resting place is a matter of great debate and theories range from accidental loss through concealment for various reasons to acts of a religious or votive nature. After a court case at which our friend Robert Lloyd Praeger gave evidence on the Crown side, the famous and important *Broighter hoard* was finally established as treasure trove and lodged in the safe-keeping of the Royal Irish Academy and the National Museum in Dublin where it can be seen on display waiting for that lucky next of kin to prove his or her line of lineage.

Another very famous hidden hoard dating from the early Christian era was found in a bog at *Derrynaflann* (the oakwoods of the Flanns) in County Tipperary. Here, on an island of good agricultural land surrounded by extensive bogland was a monastic site showing three periods of occupancy.

What a perfect place on which to build a religious sanctuary! — 28 hectares of good soil surrounded by a natural moat full of developing bog across which at one point they had to build a trackway for ease of access. Perhaps it was the trackway that let them down, for the hidden hoard of church ornaments dates to the ninth or tenth century AD when Vikings raiding the Irish coast were making straight for the riches of the monasteries. The perfect workmanship of the paten, stand, chalice and strainer show just how rich the early monastic lifestyle must have been and why such places held a special attraction for the wandering raiders. They could stock up not only on gold and silver, but also on food, clothing, weapons and utensils.

Bronze Age Hoards
Many of the bog hoards date from earlier times, and George Eogan's book on *The Later Bronze Age in Ireland* lists no less than fifty-two such finds from bogs dotted across the length and breadth of the country and dating to the middle and late bronze ages. The Irish hoards divide the bronze age into three main phases, each more affluent than the last and each showing more influence over the landscape.

The early bronze age people searched the face of Ireland for traces of the metals they needed for their technology. The scouring action of the ice had left rich veins exposed to view and as copper is toxic to the growth of most plant life, they would have remained bare of thick vegetation and so stood out even in a wooded landscape. The expertise of these first prospector farmers allowed them to recognise the signs, to mine, to smelt and to cast in bronze, using some of the implements so fashioned to dig deeper into and farm the surrounding soil.

They must have either usurped or integrated with the neolithic people who had used the land before. We do not know, but there is much evidence that they copied some of their techniques of tomb construction. Later they gave up the practice of group burials and turned to single graves with cremated remains in funerary urns well supplied with a vessel containing food and in some cases weapons for the afterlife. The fact that they were making pottery indicates that they must have been digging into the landscape in order to obtain the clay, another product of glacial action.

Hoards which were buried in the next period all contain a greater range of tools marked by better techniques of craftsmanship and especially of moulding and casting the metal objects. They also include both meat hooks and sickles thus linking their real source of affluence back to those glacial soils. With their meat and cereal they were the first barley and beef barons of Ireland. This is known as the *Bishopsland period*, so named from the town near which a most important hoard was found.

The next phase of development and likewise named after the home town of a hoard is the *Dowris period*. All such hoards relate to a greater range of tools and excellence of technique with raw materials drawn from all over Europe. Important in these finds are superbly worked bronze axes and socketed sickles. It was Professor Knud Jessen of Denmark, one of the founding champions of peatland science, who first suggested that all later bronze age finds were discovered in what had at the time been rapidly growing peat which showed little sign of decomposition, and that the older hoards were located in slower growing, more humified peat. Perhaps the new technologies of the population of the Bishopsland and Dowris peoples were enough to speed up the growth of the bogs, clearing ever larger areas of woodland and tipping the balance in favour of the bogs which then grew upwards and outwards to take down the evidence.

Fulachta Fiadh

One of the strangest objects sometimes found beneath the peat are piles of stones all of which have been badly burned, usually near small troughs set into the ground. The troughs were often lined with wood or stone and were excavated in a location in which they could be easily filled with water. Many were actually dug into alluvium or river gravels so that they would slowly fill with water seeping in through the joints of the lining. Whether self-filling or not, these convenient cooking pits (for that is what they were) were always situated close to water and so were often swallowed up by the bog.

Fulacht fiadh means 'the cooking place of the deer (or of the wild)' and they were probably first used by hunting parties who would return year after year to the same rich hunting grounds. They would light a fire to heat the stones white hot and drop them into the water. The first hiss and splutter micro-wave meat broiler which could be kept on the simmer by the simple expedient of recycling the stones.

Two superb *fulachta fiadh* have been found beneath the peat on Valencia Island and their charcoal dates to 1450 ± 90 BC and 1210 ± 90 BC. Valencia Island, situated as it is off the coast of Kerry, ranks as one of the furthest west outposts of Europe and is washed by the warm waters of the North Atlantic Drift (or Gulf Stream). Covered with forest as early as 7150 BC it must have blessed its early pastoralists with a year-round crop of grass and preliminary investigations have revealed much evidence of sub-bog walls and neolithic occupation. We can only wait with baited breath to see what further excavations will bring to the light of the twenty-first century.

Crannogs

Crannogs are artificial islands topped by a dwelling place and often a stockade, built either in lakes, swamps, marshes, fens or poor fens. Many have been swallowed up and preserved in the peat. The methods of construction were varied, but as some were built in several metres of water they must be looked upon as massive feats of civil engineering which needed much communal effort and skill to produce. In most cases the living space created on the island was not occupied by a single family, but by a whole community. The members of each crannog community, farmers, hunters and craftspeople capable of working in all the main technologies of the time, lived in symbiosis — a state of mutual help. Surrounded as they were by the preservative power of lake muds and developing peat, the artefacts they dropped or discarded became instant history and so we can learn much about each community.

Toghers and Trackways

From the evidence in the peat it can be said that wherever a bog stood in the way of, if not progress then progression from one point of interest to another, then a trackway was constructed. This at least would appear to be true in Counties Leitrim, Meath, Westmeath, Offaly, Tipperary and Galway where the vast majority of *toghers* have been found. They range from narrow pedestrian precincts to broad tracks which could safely accommodate both herds of animals and vehicular traffic. The methods of construction range from simple oak planks laid lengthways or crossways, either directly on the peat surface or on runners or sleepers, to elaborate structures laid on brushwood or gravel, some even paved with sandstone slabs. One at Bloomhill, County Offaly, runs more than a kilometre and connects the dry mineral land to a small mineral island in the centre of the bog. It is well constructed of sandstone flags, a massive operation, and was capable of taking considerable traffic.

A bit of a togher or bog road, perfectly preserved where it was build to aid transport across the developing bog about 4000 years ago. This road is from Dromard More, Co. Tipperary.

This original track, probably built around AD 1100, was overlain by 10cm of peat, upon which a second wooden track had been constructed at least in places. The wooden track was dated to AD 1200 and several thirteenth-century horseshoes were found between the two.

Another togher of note at Keenagh in County Longford is about two kilometres in length, it dates from 148 BC and was made of the wood from no less than two thousand oak trees. The oldest togher is at Corlona Bog in County Leitrim, and has been dated to 1440 ± 170 BC, proving that they were constructed as the need arose and not mainly in respect of a deterioration of climate.

Horizontal Mills

The cultivation of cereals must have added many chores to the round of agricultural life and none more chaffing than the winnowing and the grinding of the grain. The bogs of Ireland have yielded a wealth of querns and rubbers of various designs and ages. However, from early Christian times up until the modern era, simple horizontal mills flumed the power of water into the service of the farming community.

The earliest artefacts of this alternative to human muscle technology have been dated to the mid-seventh century AD. The mill in question was at Little Island in County Cork, and mention is made of such mills in the Annals of the Four Masters, at Ulster and Tighernach which date to AD 647 and 651. It is also on record that similar mills were still in use in County Roscommon in the early part of this century.

Bog Butter

Just as the horizontal mills show the importance of cereals in the Irish diet, the large caches of butter bear witness to the continuation of animal husbandry and the importance of animal products in the diet of many generations. Bog butter is one of the commonest artefacts found buried in the peat; indeed in the past it was so common that it was taken and sold as axle grease at the local markets, shades of butter mountains to come.

Finds are still being made and they vary from a few ounces to almost a hundredweight. Likewise the containers range from the bladders of sheep and cows through simple cloth or bark wrappings to elaborate decorated boxes and churns, one dated to 1789. Perhaps the most fascinating aspect of many of these finds are the faint impressions of hands, fingers and even finger prints pressed into the richness of the butter, ghosts of past affluence.

The reasons for burying the butter in the first place are as numerous as the type of container used. As most of it was unsalted, preservation in a nice cool place was probably the main reason. It has also been suggested that burial in peat could strengthen and improve the flavour. Overproduction and/or storage for lean times ahead cannot be ruled out; neither can the use of this golden commodity, prime product of a green and pleasant land, as a votive offering be discounted. As recently as the 1940s butter was always thrown into the lake at Balla in County Mayo as an act of thanksgiving for the cure of a horse or cow.

Bog Wood

As many of the raised bogs started their main period of development by overgrowing fen forest and likewise many of the blanket bogs grew where woodland had been before, it is not surprising that immense amounts of wood have been found buried in the peat. So much that when at the end of the eighteenth century much of Ireland was devoid of woodland, the poorer communities which couldn't afford to import timber turned to the bogs to supply their needs.

Such was the demand and the reward that bog wood divination developed apace. The best method was to walk the bog in the early morning, note and mark those places where there was no dew or frost lying on the bog surface. Then, using a long rod, they would probe the surface to ascertain the depth and the size of the tree trunk and determine if it had branches. Then a pit of exactly the right size was dug and the timber was removed. The absence of dew or frost in such places has never been adequately explained unless the timber was large and was very close to the surface when temperature differences would appear to be reason enough.

Uses of the wood hardened by and hard won from the bog ranged from general construction work through the crafting of furniture and domestic utensils, vessels, butter churns, milking pails and tubs for making and storing salted meat. Another use was in the manufacture of ropes used for the cording of beds and chairs and in the stitching on of the turves used in thatching houses. Here not only was the twisting of the rope a skilled and laborious job, but so was the selection and preparation of the bog wood strips.

Perhaps the strangest of all the uses of this ancient wood which had lain for so long buried in darkness was as the raw material for torches. Selected wood rich in resin would be cut into splints which were bound together and dried before use. Such a torch would continue burning even in a strong wind and so was used for late milking and as a lure to attract fish to the surface for spearing and into the nets.

Bog Bodies

Many of the bodies found preserved in the bogs are of people who either drowned in a pre-bog lake or were laid to rest by fair means or foul within the grip of the anaerobic zone *en route* to immortality and perfect preservation.

The first detailed account of a bog body found in Europe was of a body dug out of a bog near Drumkeragh in County Down in 1783. Since that first surprise event many other bodies have been found, especially in Denmark where it appears many human sacrifices were made in prehistoric times, the bodies being interred in shallow graves in the bogs (see *The Bog People* by P.V. Glob). In contrast the vast majority of the bog bodies found in Ireland are much more recent, dating from the seventeenth and eighteenth centuries and unfortunately none have so far been examined *in situ* or in the detail they deserve. A body was found under nine feet of bog in Castleblaney, County Galway in 1821:

'The face was that of a young man of handsome features and foreign aspect, and his hair which was long and black, hung loosely over his shoulders. He was dressed in a leather tunic which came as far as his knees, with laced thronging in front and tied at the neck by a band of twisted sally rods. The hair of the leather was turned inwards against the skin. On the feet were leather shoes.

An unusual feature of this bog body is the deer-skin tunic. Most bodies found in Irish bogs had woollen garments, and it is conceivable that in this case the body might be early, possibly prehistoric. If only it had been studied *in situ* and in detail, and preserved further for posterity! Sadly, few of the bog bodies found in Ireland were studied and preserved.

The dearth of bog bodies from earlier periods and cultures is strange. Could it be that the bogs, which were much less extensive in those times and were only growing very slowly, were taboo no-go areas in which they would not even bury their dead? One can only guess what else lies in wait to be discovered in the peaty record book.

CHAPTER 7:
THE TALE OF THE LITTLE RED BOG

There is no need to guess how the disjunct three-dimensional jigsaw of artefacts described in Chapter 6 finds order within the timescale of the Irish landscape. Thanks to the dedication of the pollen people, the half life of C^{14} and the myriad grains of truth lodged within the little Red Bog of County Louth, the story can now be told.

In size, Red Bog cannot compare with any of the great red bogs of the central plain. What is more it has been cut for turf and none of it can be regarded as being in pristine state. It was indeed the broad faces of the cutaways which made it extra inviting to the gallant band of peat people, led by Frank Mitchell, who came to wrest this story from its depths. They came, they saw and they took away monoliths of *Sphagnum* peat which when laid end to end reached back through more than 5000 years. A history book seven metres thick with an in-depth record of the landscape stored away within its uncut pages.

Back at the laboratory in Dublin, Professor Bill Watts took charge, lifting the 'pages' one by one, extracting the pollen, identifying and counting the grains. Exacting work, but ultra-exciting, for as each count was completed the innermost secrets of the landscape were let out of the bog.

The results are shown on the illuminated pollen diagram which covers pages x and y and more than 500 years of Ireland's history. The back bone of the diagram are the fifteen vertical columns which look not unlike those strange mirror-image insects which can be made by folding wet ink or paint in a piece of paper. Each is, however, the result of weeks of patient work, for each represents the number of grains of a certain plant or group of plants found at each level, expressed as a percentage of all the grains found at that level.

A bog acts as a passive receiver and storer of information, like a vast sheet of blotting paper which soaks up any pollen grains and spores that blow its way and fall upon its surface. The meaning of the total number of any one sort of grain is impossible to interpret, for it depends on many different factors. The amount of pollen produced by each sort of plant, the distance the pollen producers are growing away from the bog, how tall they are, how well their pollen is transported by the wind, and once it is there how susceptible it is to decay. For example a tall hazel tree with its long catkins designed by nature to shed pollen on the wind will always cloud the picture, in marked contrast to a member of the daisy flower family whose pollen is carried about by insects. The latter will always be poorly represented, even if it is growing on the edge of the peat, whereas pine, which has pollen with wing-like buoyancy bags, will travel from afar. It is for this reason that the pollen of the actual bog plants has been omitted from the diagram and percentages, not absolutes, are presented.

The pulsing columns thus represent in broad steps of decades and centuries what has happened vegetation-wise, especially on the immediate catchment of the bog. Just look at all the detail, the only problem now is its interpretation.

On the left, the data for the trees, birch, hazel, pine, beech, alder, oak, elm and ash, is presented in that order. On the right, data for a range of lesser plants, none of which would thrive under a full forest canopy, are presented for comparison. See how they complement each other, shades of changes past, forest to field and field to forest.

As each major trend of change was identified, nice large slices of peat were taken from the relevant levels to another laboratory in Trinity College, where they were dated, using the radiocarbon or C^{14} technique. This method uses the fact that all the time, even under natural conditions, radioactive carbon (C^{14}) is being produced in the atmosphere. Like all radioactive elements, the new C^{14} immediately begins to decay away until finally it all becomes good old stable C^{12} once again. This will continue to happen whether it is floating about in the atmosphere or whether it has become part of the peat. With the aid of a very sophisticated Geiger counter and the knowledge of how fast half the unstable C^{14} takes to decay away, it is possible to date peat or any other organic material.

The dates shown on the left of the diagram are all obtained using this method, the dates on the right are nominal calendar dates, that is informed guesstimates on the basis of all the information. Thus BP (before present) signifies hard radiocarbon fact, changing only with the constant updating of the technique and the base-line, the present. AD and BC on the other hand, relate to the key events of the Christian calendar and the flights of historical fact and fancy.

Once you have the data and the dates, then comes the problem of deciding what were the exact causes of each change or episode of change. The illumination of the diagram by the artist David Green is based on Frank Mitchell's interpretation which is itself based on a lifetime's work of great scholarship. All I will attempt to do here is highlight the main events, and I implore you to read *The Shell Guide to Reading The Irish Landscape* and discover for yourselves how exciting the fine details of history can be in the hands of a master. Frank Mitchell would be the first to agree that at our present state of knowledge what is presented here is a mixture of fact and fancy, but as more and more data are gathered from other sites and other bogs, the soft peat will eventually yield hard irrevocable facts.

Here follows a series of pollen headlines from the story of the little Red Bog of Louth. As you read, please check the facts against the diagram.

5500 BP

Climate probably 2°C warmer than it is today. Elm, oak, alder and pine forests are on the decline and 'scrub' birch and hazel are on the increase. Neolithic cultures were on the move across the landscape.

5200 BP

Hazel and birch 'scrub' doing well as grassland with long-leaved plantain become a more permanent feature of the landscape. Neolithic farmers rearing their animals amongst trees ring-barked using polished stone axes.

5200 to 3570 BP

Throughout this period, as elm, alder and pine wane, hazel, birch and to a lesser extent oak wax and ash, a weed tree, ready to grab the opportunity of any opening in the landscape, turns up on the scene. Different groups and cultures make use of the soils, their living systems causing cycles of forest destruction and regeneration. The big tomb operators pass on, their place taken by the more nomadic lifestyle of prospector farmers looking for copper. New lifestyles cut deeper into the forests and dig deeper into the soils using implements of bronze. Bronze and pottery must have made living much easier both for the Beaker and the Food Vessel folk, while simple single graves and cinerary urns fitted in much better with a shifting lifestyle than gigantic mausoleums. New life- and death-styles on the move. The implements found in hoards even of the early bronze age must have greatly aided the felling of trees and especially of softwoods. It is thus of great interest that by the end of this period pine pollen was no longer falling on the bog despite its built-in capabilities of long distance transport. The record in other bogs tell us that by 1000 BC pine was no longer growing in north-east Ireland and that by AD 300 the total native stock was probably near extinction.

3570 BP to 700 BC (2886 BP)

A period of much more rapid change, down go the trees, up come the shrubs and vice versa. However, it is all set against a continuous background count of grass. The grasslands are here to stay and along with them a broader spectrum of weeds, including dock and bracken. Poor old farmers — but they weren't, for this was the period of *Bishopsland* influence and affluence. Flesh hooks and sickles of fine workmanship and decoration were allowing them to reap an even richer harvest from these soils.

2625 BP to 0 BC/AD (1986 BP)
A series of hiatuses, the trees come down, the scrub grows up, in come the cereals, snap, crackle and up pops the full armory of weeds of arable land, bracken, plantain, dock, a composite bunch of daisies, dandelions, thistles, mugworts and goosefoots (or is it feet?). And just look, around 2400 BP, a supergrass job, even the hazel has been slashed back as the grass pollen shoots sky high. I only hope the local farmers didn't suffer from hay fever. At least they took heed of what the pollen count and the depletion of the soil forecast, and moved on. Then hazel, birch, ash, alder, oak and elm in that order closed in to sweep away all evidence of their fields and fortunes except for that taken down by the little Red Bog. Always there as witness before, during and after the fact.

Did the farmers of this *Dowris* period have hard graft or did they have the ard plough to help them on their way? We do not know, but digging deeper in the soil by whatever means not only helps you grow your oats but also helps the rain to leach and the deeper-rooting trees to recolonise once the fields have been abandoned.

If the climatic deterioration (wetter weather) recorded at around 2550 BP across the rest of Europe ever affected Ireland it certainly could have speeded the rate of leaching, forcing the farmers to move on. The little Red Bog shows no classic *Grenzhorizont* but by 2625 BP the rate of growth of *Sphagnum* peat had increased across the bog and the younger peats showed a better state of preservation.

Whether this was natural, Europe's climatic change coming in from the west, or whether it was the cumulative effect of the Bishopsland landscape-management or a bit of both, we may one day know. The key evidence is there, waiting to be discovered somewhere in some bog.

AD 0 to 300 (1956 BP)
The period of farming affluence apparently had come to an end. Many of the weeds disappeared, including bracken and even the grasslands were having a thin time. What had happened to cause all this? Well, Christ had been born far to the south and the Romans had conquered Gaul and Britain. Although the imperial army stopped short at the Irish Sea, warriors and others who would not put up with imperial rule at home moved out to impose their own rule on the Irish scene. So the demise of Irish agriculture could have been due simply to the disruption of the Dowris way of life by these invaders.

The reoccupation of crannogs and the epidemics of raths, sometimes called ringforts, whose remains still pockmark the face of the country, point to more than shifting agriculture taking place throughout this time. Could it be that the ard plough had done all it could, cross-scratching the soil into giving up a little more of the minerals and nutrients which had been left by glacial action now more than a hundred centuries ago. Was its usefulness now coming to an end as cycle after cycle of grass, cereals, woodland and leaching exhausted the upper layers of the soil, acidifying the upper profile, changing their nature and their utility. There is no doubt that in the wettest west such change had helped the formation of podsols, initiating the spread of blanket peat. Here in the drier east the effect is perhaps shown by the spread of birch, a tree which appears to thrive on acid heathy soil.

AD 300 to 1450 BP (c. AD 536)

Something drastic or at least dramatic must have happened: agriculture's back. Birch holding its own, while elm, oak and even ash decline and hazel crashes, recovers, then goes into prolonged decline. At the same time all the signs of farming are back in force, grass, cereals, bracken, weeds and all.

There is no record of a peace treaty or armistice to argue the case of less troubled times, and the buildings of raths complete with souterrains (bolt holes) went on apace. Likewise there is no change in rate of peat growth in which to seek an answer of drier climes; the little Red Bog went on growing at its now steady pace, taking down the incontrovertible proof that the farmers were back, perhaps with some new tool to dig deeper and more efficiently into the mineral store.

Circumstantial evidence comes from another little red bog and a crannog not far away near Dunshaughlin, County Meath. Lagore crannog was built no later than AD 650. The silts below it contain bronze age implements and the pollen record of a landscape gradually becoming dominated by heather and birch at the expense of its woodland and farmland. Then the crannog was constructed breaking the continuity of the record. However, in the mud laid down on top of the crannog mound after it had been vacated, the pollen picture has completely changed. Gone is most of the heather and some of the birch and back have come the other trees.

What is more, in amongst the remains of the crannog they found a plough share, a plough coulter, a billhook and an axe, all made of iron. The old ard plough with a wooden share made hard work of stony soil, simply bumping over the surface and having to be replaced at regular intervals. Arm the share with bronze or iron and things must improve. Provide it with a coulter cutter, a vertical blade which slices through the sod allowing the plough to dig even deeper. This may well have been the answer to the ploughman's prayer and to the AD 300 agricultural revival riddle of the little Red Bog. The plough could now reach deeper than the heather roots, tapping new sources of minerals hidden in the soil. So the heaths and trees where they still grew were replaced by the monastic way of life based on deeper furrows and faith.

There remains only one point to clarify, and that is the origin of the heather

Messages from the past — ogham stone from Aglish, County Kerry, fifth or sixth century AD. The script tells us that it was erected for the grandson of Godika. Later it was Christianised by the addition of the swastikas, symbols of the resurrection, and the cross. The bog near by can tell us much more.

at Lagore. The answer may well be hidden in the name of a small town nearby. It is Red Bog, and that is all that now remains of a bog which was probably the source of the heather pollen at the bottom of the lake and of the plants which colonised the heathland soils as they developed.

From this point on, the story told by this and all the other Irish bogs becomes clouded by history. Our understanding of prehistory is based on artefacts and hence on objectivity. They cannot tell lies, but their correct meaning can be misinterpreted until new artefacts come to light or old ones are reviewed by new techniques. Historical fact presents much greater difficulties, for any facts set down in writing have been subject to the subjectivity of one and through the plagiarising years of many human natures.

Written record, be it in primitive Latin or simple ogham script tells us that late in the fourth century people moved from Ireland to colonise what is now Wales, Cornwall, the Isle of Man and southwest Scotland. In return, Christianity came to Ireland in the fifth century and an iron shod monastic way of life changed ways and landscapes even more.

1450 BP (c. AD 536) to AD 1450

The Saxons brought pagan ways back to Britain and with them rabbits to browse in narrow fields each one furlong long. Their conversion to Christianity was helped in part by Irish missionaries who probably returned home with the latest of agricutural innovation, the mouldboard plough. The mouldboard inserts itself into the cut made by the coulter and turns the slice of earth over into the furrow made by the plough on the previous traverse. No need to cross-scratch the field any more, for a new supply of minerals is turned up onto the surface by the ploughing team, which needed to rest after each furlong, hence the word and the long thin fields. What is more, the action of the new plough buries the seeds of some weeds and lifts others to the surface, really stirring things up in a new way.

When did the little Red Bog first record effects which might be attributed to the action of the mouldboard plough? Well, somewhere about the right time, for around AD 500 elm disappears, a sure sign of expanding agriculture.

AD 800

The sagas tell us that before this time strict laws were enforced in Ireland to protect a long list of trees including all the natives. Fell an oak, hazel, ash or elm at the risk of having two milk cows confiscated. The Red Bog tells us that about this time two things popped up on the landscape dropping their pollen on the bog, elm and members of the goosefoot family of flowering plants.

Elm makes a comeback with a real burst. The fact that it was preceded by the always adventive ash and followed by oak points to the natural succession of forest regeneration on at least some of the good 'mouldboarded' soils. The fact that the forest then spread onto the poorer soils pushing out both birch and alder corroborates a long-term change.

AD 1100

Written record also tells us that as the Anglo-Norman influence spread to all the good land east of that special line which allows the soils to drain and stops the peat spreading too far beyond its basin origins, at least some sort of feudal system was in operation in eastern Ireland. Such systems were known to include within their rotation of crops the growing of large amounts of goosefoot for human consumption. And mugwort raised its aromatic head. The seeds of the mugwort are small enough to fall deep down into the cracks and crannies of a well-structured soil where they can lie dormant until lifted up into the light of another way of farming. What is more, when eaten by cows their tough coat allows them to pass right through unscathed to grow anew. Together the mouldboard, moo-cow and mugwort spread across the landscape, stirring the riches of both the soil and the monastic way of life.

The Viking raiders came and went their way as both cereals and mugwort prospered at the expense of woodlands, except those of the less ploughable soils, alder and birch. Grasslands too diminished and even bracken went into decline. Could it be that the strong farmers were now able to concentrate their efforts on the better land made more productive by the new ploughshare? Concentrating on cereals which they ground in their own water-worked mills while booleying their cattle far out of harm's way and storing their butter in the bogs. The pieces of the peat-preserved puzzle begin to fit into their proper places.

AD 1300

Written records indicate an appalling century, the weather deteriorated, Robert Bruce invaded and the Black Death came, all of which wreaked havoc. Disease and pestilence spread like wildfire, especially in the confinement of the manorial rights and wrongs. The outback areas would not have been so badly hit and so the native landowners came back from the hills and up from the bogs, pushing the foreigners back towards the coast. There they remained, almost under siege, protected by the Pale, a ditch and earthen bank, the remains of which can still be traced south from Dundalk.

The little Red Bog which lies not far from this much disputed border records these repercussions in some detail: cereals, goosefoot and grasslands including all those weeds (well, all except mugwort), disappear and hazel explodes across the landscape followed by oak — troubled times indeed for agriculture but not for the forest.

AD 1550

The Tudors, taking advantage of the booleying and bullying ways of the locals, moved in on a massive land-grab. Some bought in on the act, while a more favoured few were given large slices of Irish real estate. Sir Walter Raleigh received no less than 20,000 acres (over 8000ha) a near home base for an even richer holding in the New World, from which he had returned, complete with many new and novel things. These included two members of a family of plants poorly represented on the Irish scene. They were tobacco and the potato, the nearest Irish relative of which, the bittersweet, was probably a native of the fen forests which formed a basis for many of the raised bogs. Both tobacco and potato were destined to affect the well-being of Ireland, the latter making many like Raleigh look to the promise of new lands in America. Unfortunately, when it comes to potato pollen, the palynologists have had their chips. It cannot be identified and so as yet we do not know when this key crop first made its mark upon the Irish scene.

What we do know is that agriculture came back in an increasingly bigger way as woodlands were replaced by crops and grassland. The timber was used and exported for all manner of things from ships of the line, charcoal for the iron industry and as staves for barrels, which were in great demand for the burgeoning import-export trade of, among other things, wine and oil and salted meat.

AD 1700

By this time some two million people were living off the fat of a more settled, less wooded land. The agricultural revolution, complete with rotation of crops, was having an effect as the farmers took note of the potential of recycling. Elm, the first tree to fall to agriculture, disappeared again, and alder and hazel were drastically slashed back. Ash has popped up again and oak increases along with exotics like pine and beech planted around the domains and their demesnes. However, in this final analysis the little Red Bog appears to have let us down, at least at first sight. The weeds show a massive increase in their presence, yet we know that crop rotation had done away with the need for weed-filled fallow and seed drills placed crops in straight lines which could be hoed free of weeds. We must remember, however, that we are looking at percentages of total pollen, not absolutes: it's change that has counted all the way.

Less forest, more farm, that's what the pollen record spells out at that point in time. Yet on closer inspection woodland edge and less rough grazing land; less too of the daisies and their kin could well be a reflection of no fallow and well-weeded fields. The information is there if only we take the time to look. A peat bog tells no lies, it is not in its nature. All it can do is record the facts, facts which relate to all our pasts.

How we interpret these simple facts and how we act on what we learn will direct the course of all our futures.

CHAPTER 8:
WHAT CAN YOU DO WITH A BOG?

What can you do with 1.2 million hectares of land which is covered with some two million tonnes of organic matter which holds within its fibrous matrix the history of a nation and some forty million litres of acid, nutrient-poor water, that is approximately thirteen times the volume of Lough Neagh? The answer is one of two things: you either regard it as an insurmountable problem and leave well alone while grumbling about your misfortune, or you look upon it as a vast natural resource and lay plans for its development.

A vast natural resource of subfossil fuel equivalent to sixty thousand million million kilocalories of energy (60,000,000,000,000,000 kCal – that is the equivalent of 60,000,000,000 kilowatt hours) which covers a vast area of land which could be put to other more productive uses. So it was back in 1946, the year after a world war had drained the economy if not the spirit of so many nations that the government of Ireland faced up to the problem of peat and the Poulter Index.

Bord na Móna and the Poulter Index
Back in 1946 I was still quite a small boy and well remember that one of the main challenges of each week was the washday blues. If Monday morning hailed in a dry week then everything in both house and garden would be lovely and the washing would be complete by Tuesday at the latest. If the week was wet, then much more than hands would be wrung as the giant sycamore wood rollers of the mangle wheezed and squeezed, the whole house dripped and reeked of damp until all was safely stored in the airing cupboard. A big wash complete with sheets and blankets could become a major operation of household planning – I reckon that our family could produce about one thousandth of a hectare of washing per week, and even living in London with an average annual rainfall of only 611mm, the washday blues could last out almost until the whole cycle had to begin all over again.

Imagine then the problem of planning to dry some 100,000 hectares (the absolute maximum Bord na Móna is likely to exploit using industrial means) of sodden peat in a climate with a Poulter Index as it were designed by nature to keep the blanket always wet. The Poulter Index is a measure of the drying power of the Irish climate constructed from rainfall, sunshine and temperature data, and an understanding of this alone allowed a large section of the Irish landscape to be turned into a vast production line which could always come up with the peaty goods whatever the weather. Building a complex of workshops, railways, peat-fired power stations and an international market costs money and makes a lot of people dependent upon the success of the venture.

Sufficient areas of peatland had to be developed to ensure that whatever the deviation from the mean of the Poulter Index, there would always be sufficient turf to keep the grid lines humming and the growing international market satiated with turf. So it was that the Poulter Index and all the expertise it stood for soon became famous in the Annals of the International Peat Society. Every four years the members of the IPS gather at some appropriate venue in the peaty world to hold a conference complete with scientific and technical papers, and pre- and post-congress excursions, all of which centre around the absorbing subject of peat. At every congress there is a contingent of scientists and technicians from Ireland, who flavour the whole convivial proceedings with the fantastic breadth of Bord na Móna's knowledge concerning the peatland resources.

Bord na Móna is a government-sponsored organisation with a brief to develop the Irish peatlands for the benefit of the nation. Set up only in 1946 they have done marvels, soon putting Ireland into the world's number two position in the table of peat producers, second only to the mighty USSR which owns a staggering sixty per cent plus of the total world resources of peat. The achievements of Bord na Móna range across the whole field of the science and technology of peat and are far too numerous and technical to be recorded here.

Over the first twenty-five years of its existence, Bord na Móna surveyed, negotiated, purchased and began to develop no less than 53,000 hectares of peatland, and in 1973 was able to respond to the challenge of the fuel crisis with their imaginative 'third development programme', a plan to produce turf until the main peat resources finally run out in about 2030. This is an immense operation which has allowed the government the advantage of long-term planning both for energy and for a certain level of employment, for Bord na Móna has in recent years given employment to about 5000 full-time and 1500 part-time workers.

It would be all too easy to denigrate the whole operation by pointing out that by the year 2030, £200 million will have been invested to in effect do away with at least half a million part-time jobs by making the workers dependent on the State rather than themselves for their energy supply. To overcome any temptation in that direction, simply reach out your hand and adjust the thermostat or switch on the tumble drier, for all that back-breaking effort to win that turf has been translated into 425 megawatts of power there at the flick of a switch.

It could be argued that at no time during the lifetime of Bord na Móna has there ever been any direct economic advantage in using turf for the generation of electricity. Other primary sources could have been used and the electricity would have been produced just as cheaply. However, this simplistic argument can easily be counteracted by the many advantages. For a start, this energy is produced without any of the pollution problems inherent in coal- or oil-fired or nuclear power plants. What is more, a home-based fuel economy is immensely valuable.

Third Development Programme

The aim of this was an annual production of 6 million tonnes of milled peat, seventy per cent for electricity and thirty per cent for briquettes, 2.8 million cubic metres of moss peat and a maintained output of 0.9 million tonnes of sod peat at least up until the end of the twentieth century. The production of milled peat will peak in 1990, after which it will decline. Briquette production should peak before and be maintained until 2010; sod peat production will slowly decline and end in 2006 and exploitation of the available peat resources will be complete no later than 2030.

However, one important aspect of all this is the promise of more land for development in various ways, once the peat deposits have been worked out. It is almost as if 100,000ha of land have been waiting as they did throughout the last ice age for the light and warmth of a new productive spring. The only difference is that they are not freshly ground rock debris full of mineral promise but soils which have lost many of their useful minerals. However, mixed with a planned overburden of peat, be it fen or bog, the promise is there for a new green revolution. In this respect Bord na Móna has not shirked its responsibilities, for a key part of its overall plan has been to carry out research into the problems and potentialities of agriculture, horticulture and forestry on the cutaway bogs.

Bord na Móna's original plans contained nothing pertaining to conservation, even of key sites, but why should they? They were laid back in 1946 when the world was still regarded as a gigantic place overflowing with natural resources. Even their third development programme was couched under the constraints of an energy crisis which could have sparked off a third world war, and seven years before the world conservation strategy was officially launched. Their role in the exciting future of the Irish peatland resource must, however, encompass conservation.

Conservation and the Future

If Bord na Móna will have developed no more than ten per cent of the total peatland resource of Ireland by the year 2030, why should there be any worries about conservation? Surely the ninety per cent that will be left is more than sufficient? Unfortunately the problems of large-scale mechanised peat production and the geography of the Poulter Index limit such economic operations to certain types of peat complexes, namely groups of the largest ridge-raised bogs and flood-plain bogs, so the best of these have already gone or are ear-marked for development. What is more, turf-cutting and drainage didn't start in 1946. It had been going on for centuries, slowly but surely nibbling away at the resource, so much so that fifty-one per cent of the total resource has already been cut away or afforested and a large proportion of the remainder has been so altered by drainage, overgrazing and erosion that it is no longer of direct use for conservation, while the rest is being developed at the rate of about 9000ha a year.

Afforestation of unmodified peatland has gone on apace since 1974, being carried out almost entirely by the Forest and Wildlife Service. Practically all the blanket bogs are now adversely affected by sheep rearing, which includes grazing, trampling and burning. This is thought to be responsible for a loss of the diversity of both their plant and animal communities, and an acceleration if not the causation of the severe and widespread erosion of mountain blanket peats.

A surge of development due to grants to private developers under the Turf Development Act 1981 was alone responsible for over 4800ha being developed in the following year. In particular it is expected that development of the western raised bogs will be speeded up as Bord na Móna exhausts the midland raised bogs. If one assumes that all the activity now occurring on the midland raised bogs was then switched to the western bogs, all raised bogs would be gone in seventeen years. The position of the raised bogs is obviously critical. However, the facts above understate the seriousness of the situation. Remember, not all the remaining bogs are worth conserving. Recent surveys by the Forest and Wildlife Service have indicated that at the present rate of exploitation all raised bogs east of the Shannon will be gone by 1989.

An overall strategy for conservation is now desperately required and has in fact been called for by the European Parliament. Let us hope that all concerned, including the government, Bord na Móna, the Forest and Wildlife Service and non-government organisations like An Taisce, the Irish Wildlife Federation and the Irish Peatlands Conservation Council start working together on such a strategy before it is too late.

Timothy Hickey and the Gearagh

Before 1952 a large area of wet native forest existed south of Macroom in County Cork. It was known as the 'Gearagh' (wooden river) and the praises of the wet

BORD FAILTE

Pl. 49 World heritage in sight. . . High cross at Moone, Co. Kildare c. AD 800.

Ireland's heritage of worked stone is second to none. It tells of both pagan and Christian societies, which dug ever deeper into the soils of Ireland to raise crops and build new ways of life. Not far from each monument is a bog which not only warmed the hearths of laity and saints alike, but took down the evidence of their presence on the land in the finest of detail.

SLIDE FILE

BORD FÁILTE

Pl. 50 The Gearagh as seen from the air. This is a wet wonderland of forest and open water, a glimpse of what much of Ireland was like when people arrived on the scene. Despite its uniqueness, and its special place in Irish literature and folklore, much of the site was destroyed in 1953. However, part of it lives on and has a champion called Timothy Hickey, a young conservationist who has much to teach his elders.

Pl. 51 Picture postcard peat. . . Greetings from Ireland: turf stacked to dry in the 115-plus drying days of the wetter west of Ireland. The donkey would rather carry fum, but the creels can take the weight of the good black peat.

RICHARD MILLS

53

Pl. 52 For cutaway reed potential. . . A dense stand of common reed provides cover for a family of ducks and a good crop for those with the sense to realise its potential. Large areas of cutaway produced by Bord na Móna and other developers will need to be drained by pumps if they are to be turned over to farming or forestry. Why not plant them with reeds and use reed powder to fuel the power stations of the future? Experiments are under way to prove it possible.

Pl. 53 Pollution control. . . Reedmace growing in a cutaway. These plants grow fast in wet places, especially if the water is enriched with nutrients. They don't mind other forms of pollution either, and as they grow they help to cleanse the water. The only problem is what to do with all the biomass (organic matter) so produced. How about turning it into electricity?

138

Pl. 54 *Shadows in the cutaway. . . Winning turf reveals layers in the bog. The living floating skin or scraw, the light brown 'flow' or 'fum' and the dark black heavier peat which is ideal for fuel. The old process of turf-cutting is the same all over the country, but the tools of the trade — the slains and the barrows — differ in design.*

Pl. 55 *Plug into peat power . . . the energy laid down by the bog plants of the past is converted into the flick-of-a-switch convenience of electricity. Thanks to the expertise of Bord na Móna and their understanding of the Poulter Index, a cottage industry has provided a nation with a slice of the power it needs. Well done! . . . but what about the future?*

Pl. 56 Anser albifrons. *This beautiful white-fronted goose breeds in Greenland and overwinters in Scotland and Ireland. It spends its winter nights resting in pools and soaks upon the bogs, and its day feeding in the callows and shallows. This bird is now on the endangered list because its winter roosting sites are being destroyed. We expect desperately poor third world countries to look after their big game — come on Ireland, do your bit!*

RICHARD MILLS

140

Pl. 57 Ancient and modern. . . Coppice with standards is an ancient form of woodland management. Two hundred hectares of cutaway planted and managed by this method could supply a one-megawatt power station with all its needs and some 6000 good hardwood trees every seventy years. With some 400,000 hectares of cutaway looking for a future that future could indeed be bright.

PETER LOUGHRAN

Pl. 58 *Unreal estate. . . A cutaway reveals it all. The dark and light layers indicate periods of slow and rapid growth of the peatland resource, fifty-five per cent of which has already been cut away, afforested or so altered that it is of no use to conservation. Development continues apace at the rate of 9000 hectares a year. What happens when the peat runs out and what do you do with all the cutaway?*

Pl. 59 *Bord na Móna — No. 2 in the peat stakes. . . If you are going to supply even part of a nation's needs by turning turf into electricity, you must have the vision, the know-how and the machinery. Bord na Móna are now No. 2 in the world when it comes to winning peat, beaten to the peaty post only by Russia. By the year 2030 they will have cut away almost 100,000 hectares. What then?*

SLIDE FILE

Pl. 60 Sausage machines. . .? 'Sausages' of peat laid out to dry upon the living surface of the bog. Claims are made that new techniques allow peat sausages to be extracted, leaving the living skin intact. If this were true, the future for many aspects of this rich resource would be assured. However, there are grave doubts and proof is needed that irreparable damage will not be done.

DECLAN DOOGE

144

wilderness were sung by botanists, zoologists, writers and poets. Gibbings's 'Sweet Cork of Thee' and 'Lovely is the Lee', An t-Athair Peadar Ó Laoghaire's *Mo Scéal Féin*, Cross's *The Taylor and Ansty*, Coalman's *Journeys into Muskerry* and the music of Seán Ó Riada all speak in elegant terms of its part in Ireland's cultural heritage. Studies by scientists like Praeger, Tansley, Braun-Blanquet, Tuxen, Lodi and other members of the Ninth International Plant Geographic Excursion sang its praises as ancient post-glacial alluvial forests unique in Ireland or Britain and of very rare occurrence in Europe.

It was a wonderful place of oak woodland, fen and a maze of waterways in which many a traveller and time had lost itself, a place in which the mesolithic people would still have felt at home and renegades like Seán Rua na Gaoire and many *poitín* makers had sought and found refuge.

Despite its international importance it was flooded in 1953 as part of a hydroelectric scheme and many mourned its loss. However, one young scientist by the name of Timothy Hickey, finding that all was not lost and that regeneration was taking place, became its champion.

I received a letter in 1984 from Timothy telling me all about his efforts and ideas to save the Gearagh. Macroom Council felt the area was an eye-sore and that it should be turned into a lake for recreational activities. This was Timothy's reaction:

On hearing this, it infuriated me and frankly I didn't believe it was possible that people would try and destroy the area again. As the story goes I went to the Macroom Council and explained to them how rare and unique the area still is. After explaining to them as best I could, the answer I was given was, 'You're nothing but a school kid who knows nothing about this area and mind your own business.' When I heard this I knew that they wouldn't listen to reason, so I knew that in order to get this area conserved I had to have publicity and proof to back up what I knew. The report consisted of recordings of plants, insects and birds, some of which are rare natives of West Cork.

Well, I knew by entering competitions that it meant publicity and getting to know people that might help me. I never expected to win the Aer Lingus Young Scientists Exhibition, but when I did, the Council took a new approach to me because finally they realised the area after all was still very unique.

Timothy's report on the Gearagh points out its importance as a wintering ground for wildfowl and a refuge for a unique and diverse flora — a very special habitat, but under threat from tree-felling, over-shooting and encroaching industrial development. Timothy went on to suggest that the area could be developed as a biological study area for the local schools and indeed Timothy's own school has set up a laboratory there.

He also suggested that the field laboratory principle could be extended to educate

145

the general public about ecology, and that the area might be made into a large open-air classroom for use by all. The area could be made a wildlife sanctuary and the woodland preserved.

Timothy Hickey's report on the Gearagh is a remarkable document in every way, and if I believed in reincarnation I would say that in this young mind are lodged all the attributes of Robert Lloyd Praeger himself. It is a document of hope written by one so young that he can carry that hope into the reality of a green growing future. We can all learn lessons on conservation from Timothy's example.

Ireland is thrice blessed. It has green landscape with great capabilities, it has a small population which has not gone too far down the road of abject addiction to industrialisation, and it has a heritage of wilderness, prehistoric and early Christian artefacts which are not bettered anywhere else in Europe. What is more they have not as yet been subjected to the subsidised vandalism of arable farming, which has in recent years destroyed so much in lowland Britain. Now Ireland has the potential of new land within its grasp, its own inner space which has lain hidden and protected for thousands of years and is now, thanks to Bord na Móna, ready to be developed for the benefit of all future generations.

The Way Ahead
The most pressing decisions concern the protection of what remains of the Gearagh and of the sites listed in Appendix 2. The list was drawn up after extensive survey and exhaustive discussion and deliberation with international experts by J.B. Ryan and J.R. Cross of the Forest and Wildlife Service. If all were protected in their entirety then Ireland would have fulfilled her international obligations and indeed would lead the world in peatland conservation. If we estimate that a few more sites will be added to the list as more detailed information comes to light and round the figure off to 50,000ha, it would even then amount to only just over four per cent of the total resource. As far as the ridge-raised and flood-plain bogs are concerned, it is a mere 1.3 per cent of their ultra-valuable, ultra-exploitable area.

If only it had been done back in the 1950s when such land fetched around £5 per hectare! Then it could have been accomplished for a mere £250,000 — what an investment! Even at today's inflated price of around a hundred times as much, the total cost would still only be £30 million, which is not a great deal, even in these tough times, to pay in order to meet our international obligations to conservation. 'Only £30 million,' I can hear the pink paper pundits exclaim, '£30 million in these non-financial times, we need the energy, we need the land, we need the money for development.'

Development of what? Silicon valleys, high tech industries, science parks? The clean dust-free environments of the boglands should offer ideal sites, sitting as they do upwind from polluted Europe. There is, however, the other side to this particular economic coin, the immense value of the boglands in their own right.

Thanks to the promise of computers, robotics and microprocessors, the world is moving away from the ways of even light satanic sweat-shops towards new economies based on leisure and service. The world's number one growth area is human population — it will double in the next thirty years — and the world's number one growth industry is leisure. In stark contrast, the world's most rapidly disappearing resources are agricultural land in good heart and unpolluted wilderness, untouched by the stamp of the twentieth century.

Ireland still has untamed catchments with winding rivers and bogs, fens, callows and marshes all at least in semi-natural order without the straight lines and square corners of development or the main taints and tints of pollution. Wide open landscapes unmarred by the order of crops or plantations, a corner of Europe which still breathes the welcome of wilderness to all those yearning for respite from the pressures of modern living.

In 1980, international tourists — more than two and a half million — brought no less than £278.7 million into the country. In the same year £169.3 million of the country's wealth was redistributed by the Irish enjoying Ireland and the total industry accounted for more than nine per cent of all the jobs in the country. The fact that a large proportion of those jobs were maintained in the less economically developed areas of the west and south-west, speaks of the importance of conservation of those peatland landscapes and everything they contain.

A World Heritage Site
The whole of the blanket bog fringe, where in neolithic times the grass grew lush and green twelve months of each year, should be designated and managed as a world heritage site. It fulfils all the main criteria necessary for inclusion on the list: uniqueness of wildlife, wilderness and cultural heritage. It deserves to stand alongside Mount Everest, the Californian Redwoods, the Pyramids, the South West Tasmanian Wilderness and all the others basking in the recognition and the protection they deserve.

Beaches as clean and white as any in the world, lapped by the warmth of pure Atlantic waters which are alive with marine life from seaweeds through shellfish to sharks, dolphins and whales. Clear rivers and lakes, which, but for poaching, both national and international, would rival any other game fishery in the world. They are fortunately still home to a thriving coarse fishery and to myriad wildfowl. Haphazard fields and hedgerows, thickets and copses, all with a diversity of wildflowers and fruits each in due season to welcome birds in their millions. These include the lucky residents, the regular migrants and the rare visitors who drop in from time to time, sending more than a flutter through the ever growing ranks of the birdwatching fraternity.

Here is the landscape which helped inspire William Butler Yeats. Here too the

147

landfall of the first transatlantic flight safe within the vastness of the great peat blanket which is only now revealing secrets which it has kept safe for 5000 years or more. Secrets of all our pasts.

Here lies a complete record of the first agricultural revolution, and the signs of abject failure as 'beef' gave way to 'barley', proving not for the last time that large tracts of Ireland are better suited to contented cows than to the cowboys of agribusiness. In those same degraded soils are the roots of pagan faiths which paved the way towards the worship of one God which gave us dominion over all other things.

A New Tourist Industry for Ireland

The Grand Tour of Ireland could start in no better place than amongst those field systems which first fed cattle, then Mammon, then God, in that order. From there it would be a case of take your pick from Carrowmore, Creevykeel, Magheraaghannish, Altdrumman, Beaghmore, Kilclooney More, Poulnabrone, Baur South, Poulaphouca, Newgrange, Knowth, Annaghmore, Coomaltoukane, Drombohilly, Punchestown, Turoe, Castlestrange, Killycluggan and so many more. The pagan faiths made use of the whole wealth of the country and leave us wondering at their industry and the meaning of their standing stones and ogham script.

All that is just a start, for it is possible to follow those faiths into a new millennium enlightened by the birth of Christ. Christianity came to a land devoid of any towns, yet pockmarked with crannogs and raths, no less and probably many more than a quarter of a million of the latter. So it was that monasteries mushroomed and tall decorated crosses became the symbol of deeper faith and deeper soil-borne prosperity.

Skellig Michael (Sceilg Mhichíl), Gallarus, Monasterboice, Clonmacnoise, Kilmachcluagh, Duiske, Holycross, Dysart O'Dea, Mellifont, Killaloe, Ardmore, Clonfert, Teampall Bhéanan and Breachin and again many, many more. Each one a special part of Ireland's heritage of welcome, hosannahs in an oratorio of stone and not far from each a bog which has not only helped to warm the hearths of saints and laity alike but which has taken down the evidence of their presence where even here on earth moth and rust cannot corrupt. Why even the rhetoric of Abban, Ciarán, Declan, Palladius (first emissary from the Pope), Columba, David, Patrick and all the others who confessed their sins, said prayers and sang praises are there encapsulated in the past. Carbon dioxide they exhaled will have been taken up by the bogland plants to be fixed within the substance of the peat, rubrics in these reliquaries of a changing landscape.

Yet to date little of this wealth of artefact and growing knowledge is made available to even the discerning visitor. There is no matrix of information centres, no chain of reconstructed settlements, no herds of primitive cattle or sheep, no pagan or Christian tourist routes marked out and serviced to interpret the great wealth of heritage.

Every time I go to the airports of Shannon, Dublin or Cork, I search in vain for real souvenirs. Bog oak of immense age and perfect preservation, why burn it all when some could be turned to better use? Slices of peat, pages from that history book could be authenticated and dated to each key event. Surely a slice of living history laid down when St Patrick breathed that way is better than a plaster model. If the emigrants took turf from their home bog with them when they went to settle in the far corners of the earth, their descendants who return to find their roots should not be denied the possibility to do the same.

If machines can make peat briquettes, so they can compress and bond Celtic or other artefacts from peat laid down at the exact time those cultures thrived. Newspaper headlines and accounts concerning the great bog bursts, the great hunger when starving people tried in vain to grow potatoes on the peat which still contains the spores of *Phytophora infestans* (potato blight), small vials of bog butter must be worth more than axle grease, and even bog water coloured golden brown can be marketed for what it is, the humic essence of history. Having produced the first whiskey in the world, the Irish have no need to add the flavour of peat smoke. They should, however, be proud of the fact that the water which puts life into *uisce beatha* is an infusion of their history for it passed through peat-covered catchments on its way to the maltings and distilleries. So much more could be done to open the eyes, the minds and the purses of the tourist to all this and yet like them I have to content myself with model shillelaghs and plastic leprechauns.

My apologies for having to be so mercenary, but this is perhaps the saddest aspect of these modern times that everything must be made and seen to pay its way. I will continue to sing the praises of peat and peatlands in any way I can for they are of immense and increasing value for so many reasons. Yet to many, and unfortunately to many in authority, they are still regarded as no more than an encumbrance, something to be feared even to be ashamed of, a blight on the landscape and the lives of its people.

An Investment for the Future

People are set apart from all the other products of creative evolution by and through the power of conscious thought. We alone can learn from history, be it natural or people-made, and we alone can put what we learn to good account. An understanding of history and a sense of heritage are cornerstones of both civilisation and of the Christian faith. God's first commandment, written firm in the Book of Genesis, is for us to have dominion over all other living things and that includes the living communities of the bogland. Dominion is wise rule, conservation is wise use. Together they can save that last four per cent and so much more.

It is not much to ask as an investment for all our futures which are going to be steeped in more leisure time. The realisation of certain aspects of the peatland resource, Bord na Móna style, will have taken ninety years, providing jobs for perhaps 20,000 people and energy for many more. The challenge is now to develop the rest of the resource in such a way that it will be of lasting benefit. Conservation doesn't threaten jobs, it creates them. Management of that precious four per cent and the heritage aspect of the resource requires the expertise of gamekeepers, landscape architects, designers, historians, archaeologists, writers, actors, guides, hoteliers, restaurateurs, craftspeople, engineers, all working together to translate the story of the living history books into the wealth-creating reality of the true Irish experience.

The first and crucial step down this positive green growing road is the complete protection of the listed sites (Appendix 2) before it is too late.

These are the best sites left as surveyed by the scientists of the Forestry and Wildlife Service. All have been shown to be good viable examples and together they represent a cross section of the main types of peatland found in Ireland. If they and their catchments are protected and managed in the right way the uniqueness of the living tapestry of Ireland's bogs will be there for the benefit of science, education and aesthetic pleasure of future generations. What is perhaps even more important, the core of the genetic stock of those peatlands will be safe. Although the vast majority of the species of plants and animals which make up the peatlands are not unique to Ireland (they are indeed found in many other countries), the populations of each are, however, unique, for they have been selected throughout time to be successful and productive under the special conditions of soil, peat and climate. They are the survivors on the Irish scene and will, given the chance, always grow, protecting the soils and the peats from erosion. Natural regeneration with native genetic stock is always an important part of landscape management. It saves the expense of introducing and pampering other plants which are not specially adapted to the rigours of the local scene. The native bog plants will have an ever increasing part to play as the rest of the peatland resource is developed, whatever line is taken.

CHAPTER 9:
CUT AND THRUST —
OPTIONS FOR THE FUTURE

The research carried out by Bord na Móna and other institutes on the potential of both cutaway and virgin bog for development, though limited by funding, has addressed the main problems in a rigorous way. The options would appear to be either agriculture or forestry and both are fraught with problems, both natural and people-made.

Farming the Bogs?
It must be the dream of every ministry of agriculture to have at its disposal some 100,000 hectares of new land for development. This is especially true in a country like Ireland in which more than two-thirds of the land is used for farming and yet a quarter of the farmers work very small holdings.

If you are able to spend enough time, energy and money you will be able to grow anything anywhere, but it's a different matter when you have to realise an economic return on your investments. In the halcyon days of all sorts of subsidies almost anything was possible. However, amongst the stark reality of milk lakes and butter and cereal mountains the EEC now holds the view that production aids should only go to enterprises that are potentially commercial because otherwise they only serve to aggravate surplus production. So proof is needed and research has shown that it is not easily come by.

Development of virgin blanket bogs of any type for agriculture is a non-viable proposition. Any such venture can be likened to pouring capital down an ever widening drain flushed by 1250mm of slightly acid rain even in an average year. Cutover blanket bog offers a little more hope, yet even with expensive drainage, grading and fertilisation the resultant grass or croplands are open to all sorts of problems. In the existing climate of rain days and rainy days ahead the best maxim is when it comes to planting crops leave the blanket bogs well alone.

Turning to raised and ridge-raised bogs, the same applies to the virgin territories, but the cutaways, especially those being produced by Bord na Móna, offer some hope. The best areas, especially those underlain by woody fen peat, can be improved to produce grade one agricultural soils and at least some of these will probably be turned over to a range of crops. However, to keep them in good heart, drains will have to be rigorously maintained, opening the peat up to leaching, shrinkage and decay, so even the woody peat will be a wasting asset and down below is solid sticky clay. At the other end of the cutaway scale there is already clay, and large areas that will require pumped drainage to keep them dry. These must fall into the non-viable category. Also, the 1.5 million hectares of land now being farmed urgently requires drainage to reach its full agricultural potential, so the future for agriculture on peat begins to look bleak.

Forestry
There is no getting away from two contrasting facts. Most of the landscapes of Ireland which are now covered with peat supported the growth of trees in the not too far distant past. Yet, today, apart from Iceland, Ireland has the least forest cover of any country in Europe, a miserable five per cent.

The first attempt to grow trees on virgin peatland was way back in 1892 when 500ha at Knockboy in County Galway were opened up for silviculture (growing trees). It was a dismal failure and site selection was to blame. From that time on, successive administrations tried to put forestry high on the list of national priorities and as high on the mountains as practicable.

A target for a national policy of afforestation was set at 400,000ha to be planted in forty years, on the basis of an FAO (Food and Agriculture Organisation) report submitted in 1951. This recommended that half of the forested land should be fully 'commercial' and half of it 'social' forestry, the one providing a profit, the latter employment in the western counties, together cutting down the enormous costs of wood import bills. With such a prodigious target and with the cost and problems of land acquisition, the afforestation of bogland soon became an integral part of the plan.

One of the first real problems was indeed the pattern of land acquisition, for although small scattered blocks of woodland are not without some merit in a landscape, the cost of fencing them adequately against grazing animals became prohibitive. No wonder, then, that the wide open spaces of the blanket peats, where forestry plus ring fences appeared an economic possibility, came high on the list. 1982 saw 140,000ha of virgin blanket bog drained and turned over to trees with plans to plant another 100,000ha of similar terrain. This is in marked contrast to the mere 6350ha of virgin raised bog on 21,500ha of cutaway planted to date. All in all, it adds up to a fantastic achievement, but those last figures give cause for concern.

There are two reasons why virgin raised bog is so low on the plantation lists: the cost of afforestation of deep peat and the value of the peat itself. Peat is of immense value if only from the point of view of the potential energy it represents.

Once a peat resource is covered with trees, that potential is at least temporarily lost.

In order to win the peat, a bog must be drained and the product left to the vagaries of the Poulter Index. During the period of exploitation, the drainage characteristics and the water quality of the catchment (the valley in which the bog is situated) will be altered. In order to turn a bog into a plantation, it must be drained, limed and fertilised, all of which will again alter the characteristics of water flow in the rivers and the chemistry of their waters. What is more, these effects will be spread over a long period, for if any aspect of the management lapses the trees will only grow slowly, or not at all. In the same way that a catchment comes into equilibrium with its bogs, so too will it come into equilibrium with its new forests. Dense plantation of conifers may well acidify the waters and affect their quality in other ways to the detriment of their ecology and their fisheries. It is therefore fortunate that the whole operation is in the hands of officers of the Department of Fisheries and Forestry, who should have a mutual vested interest in keeping the landscape chemistry just right. The same should also apply to the whole resource equation.

Bord na Móna's research into the afforestation of cutaway raised bog peat at Clonstat in County Offaly showed that sitka spruce could yield 24 cubic metres of wood per annum — a staggering figure, for average yields for Ireland are only 16 cubic metres per annum. The work is also yielding equally promising results with other species of trees. Their experiments indicate that in general between 1 and 1.3 metres of peat should be left in order to obtain the best results. Results obtained from raised bogs, especially where they are underlain by wood and fen peats which are not as acid and contain a good store of minerals are also very promising. In these cases only 60cm of peat need be left in order to get the trees to grow.

One hectare of land covered with a metre of peat represents 10,000 cubic metres of potential saleable product. To realise the same amount even in sitka spruce would take around 400 productive years. That is at least nine cycles of tree growth, each cycle being fraught with the costly practices of drain maintenance, liming, fertilisation, pest and fire control, all of which can lead to pollution of the waterways and do lead to shrinkage, wastage and erosion of the peat base. How 'commercial' then is any of this forestry, and on the social side would it not be best to subsidise the hand-winning of the total peat resource, and then remineralise the soils beneath and start the whole process off all over again?

This question brings us on to what is perhaps the most fascinating aspect of the research carried out to date by Bord na Móna and others. This has addressed itself to the novel concept that such areas could be developed for short-term rotation forestry, or turned over to the ancient and well-proven practice of coppice and pollard management. The peat record tells us in graphic detail that mixed forest once thrived on many of the bogland sites and links people pressure and

153

climatic change to its replacement by pine and peat. Pine, be it natural or planted, only grows from seed, and so one crop of individuals must be replaced by another. This is unfortunately true for all the fast growing conifers, and although they can be grown for just their first few most productive years, each short cycle of harvesting and replacement will cause at least some of the upheavals and problems of a long-term crop. Conifers are not amenable to coppicing or pollarding.

Coppicing is an ancient practice which turns trees into multistemmed bushes by cutting back almost to ground level at intervals of between five and twenty-two years. Pollarding is probably an even more ancient practice which leaves a short tree trunk to protect the regular harvest of branches and twigs from the attention of animals of the browsing kind.

Many trees like willow, hazel, elm, oak and ash, all of which were components of the original Irish mixed forest and others like lime, hornbeam and sweet chestnut which have been introduced, all thrive on such maltreatment. All also give good harvests of small wood and wood wastes, cycle after cycle after cycle with no need to clear fell and replant, no need to open up the soil to leaching and erosion. What is more the pulsed cycle of growth of deciduous trees along with the rich ground fauna and flora they support, appears to be less harsh on the waters which seep through its aegis; they do not become so acid.

Experiments set up in the north in 1974 growing willow on peat yielded a promising 12 tonnes per hectare, which could be used for either paper pulp or energy production. Experiments set up at Bellacorick in County Mayo were aimed at keeping a specially converted five-megawatt power station fired with wood from some 600ha of short rotation forest on peat. Unfortunately they have now been abandoned because the current low price of other forms of fuel indicated that the growing of fuel in this form would not be economically viable.

Overlooking such short-term thinking and working on the proven production capacity of coppice, 200ha would be sufficient to service a one-megawatt power station with all its fuel needs. The 100,000ha which could become available by the projected termination of Bord na Móna's peat-winning operations, could, under coppice, service a 500-megawatt power station. This is a very conservative estimate, for other figures now being bandied about in the literature indicate a figure of 1200 megawatts from the same area. Many other countries are now actively investigating such methods of energy farming, for all now realise that the world's stocks of fossil fuels are finite and expensive. The same is true of uranium. The only way ahead is to create and maintain growing resources which are renewable. For those who say, 'Why bother, science will discover and develop a new cheap safe source of energy?' the answer is still the same. Plant trees for the future, because once we have used up all the coal, oil, natural gas and peat we will have to grow the organic chemicals we need as raw materials for our plasto-chemical way of life. Forests for ever and ever — it can and must be done.

154

Benefits of the Coppice Cycle

The positive aspects of such short-term continuous forestry development are many. Such forests give a much quicker return on the investment of both capital and land, not only in terms of wood production, but also in the letting of amenity and game rights. Coppice woodlands provide continuous cover for the soil, protecting it from erosion and the streams, rivers and lakes it feeds from adverse change.

The coppice cycle enhances the chances of a whole range of woodland life, birds, animals, insects, flowers, ferns and mosses to name but a few. The oakwoods of Killarney, now under threat from an epidemic of introduced rhododendron, are not only great tourist attractions, but are also the last stronghold of Ireland's woodland flora and fauna. The new coppice woodlands would help expand their territories. The fact that they are diverse living systems and not artificial monocultures reduces the chance of epidemics and hence cuts down the need for costly methods of disease and pest control. The challenge to the chemical companies will be to use their tremendous expertise in developing new products which work alongside nature, enhancing production beyond the already proven limits.

If you prune the shoots of a plant, the roots will grow in strength, seeking out deeper supplies of minerals and water, binding the soil together. What is more, without the need to support tall straight trunks and massive canopies, coppice is not as susceptible to wind-throw or to fire as trees grown in plantations. Such woodland also has the advantage of being able to support a whole range of crafts and craftspeople – tool and furniture-making, wood-turning, fencing, thatching, hurdling, the glazing of pottery and the making of preserves and sachets of natural fruits and herbs.

So why, if everything in the coppice garden looks so lovely, isn't everybody jumping in on this bandwagon? The answer is that some are, but many are having first to count the cost of the missing infrastructure. How do you create the rural communities which will respond well to the demands of what is in fact a production-line ethic: enough wood must be grown and it must be provided on time. How do you link the diffuse 'cottage' production lines and transport their products to the power plants?

In Ireland much of it is already in place and already happening, thanks to Bord na Móna and the Department of Fisheries and Forestry. The workshops and the roads and narrow-gauge tracks are there, as is the rural workforce, keeping up the necessary supply to those peat-fired stations. The former are doing well with younger generations eager to follow in their parents' broad tracks. Many of the latter are, however, showing signs of aging and are ready to be made more efficient and could be converted to coppice power. Ireland has helped lead the world through the pay days of peat power, sending its experts and its expertise to give wise counsel across the world. She can now fulfil a similar role in developing this new branch of biotechnology, for that is exactly what it is. Coppice management promises a green and growing future.

Now expand the concept to all the other areas of Irish peat which have already been altered by the winning of part of its resource. If we consider only the 85,600ha of cutaway lowland blanket bog, the 172,000ha of cutaway raised and ridge-raised bog and the 57,100ha that is the lowland half of the cutaway mountain blanket bog the grand total of potential coppice could produce 2000 megawatts of power. (These figures are based on 1974 statistics relating to privately owned cutaway.) The final icing on the hypothetical but practicable cake comes if all was managed under the rules of coppice with standards. In medieval times, laws in Britain ensured that in each hectare of coppice thirty good straight trees were selected and left to grow to maturity, rarely beyond. If this same principle were applied to these proposed Irish holdings then lucky timber merchants of a not too far distant future could be dealing with no less than 171,000 home-grown hardwood trees every year.

There are, of course, immense problems in bringing all this to fruition, not the least being that of persuading landowners and governments that the development of coppice is going to turn the clocks forward not back — it's all part of the biotechnological revolution. Brewing, baking, leather-making, although ancient crafts, are now the focal points of multi-million dollar biotechnological industries, although the basic principles have not changed. Likewise woodburning stoves and charcoal burners may have a folksy image, but properly designed and engineered to carry out the destructive distillation of wood they soon become marvels of biotechnological advance.

One thousand kilogrammes of wood can produce 50kg of tar, 38kg of acetic acid, 15kg of methanol, 40 cubic metres of gas, a whole range of lesser products including acetone and alcohol and 250kg of charcoal. The former products often go up the flue unburned, causing problems on the way. The latter product is the most efficient fuel there is, and when mixed with even the lowest grades of coal effectively reduces their polluting qualities. It's all part of coppice biotechnology, a wealth of warmth and raw materials for chemical industries yet to put down new roots, all they are waiting for is the grow-ahead.

Another bogland crop of the future goes under the cosmopolitan name of *Phragmites australis* or common reed. A native plant of Ireland and much of the rest of the world it still grows in luxuriant abundance along the margins of lakes and rivers as it did before the fens and bogs started to form. It is also one of the first plants to colonise certain types of cutaway where it forms dense stands providing protection for a range of waterfowl and other birds and a habitat for other members of the peat-dwelling flora and fauna.

Experiments in Scandinavia and more recently at the Mount Dillon Bord na

Móna works near Lanesborough are showing it to be a viable energy crop which can be mechanically harvested using special machinery which does not damage the peat surface. No drainage is necessary, in fact the reed thrives under waterlogged conditions and will effectively help cleanse polluted water stripping out many of the nutrients and then holding them in cycle. The crop is harvested in winter when it has a water content of only twenty per cent as compared to milled peat with a water content of fifty-five percent. The reed is harvested and milled by the machines and the 'reed powder' can fuel the power stations with little modification.

Even more exciting are new biotechnological developments which can turn the reed, along with other straw waste, into a wood substitute which has the capabilities of both extrusion and moulding. The future looks bright indeed for reed culture and such reed beds would be excellent for nature conservation and hold enormous potentialities for fish culture and fish farming.

Peat with Value Added

The peat and peatlands of Ireland have for too long been regarded in a negative way, a soggy legacy from the past, a boggy problem for the future. Bord na Móna has done more than its fair share to show it all in a more positive light; the time is now ripe for a total re-think about the rest of the resource before it is too late.

Across the length and breadth of the continent of Europe, spa towns are situated close to large peatlands and many people go not only to take their waters and peat bath therapies, but also to rest, exercise and recuperate amongst the tranquil beauty of the peatland setting. It may be that there is some curative property in the peat (Stanislauf Tolpa, who first classified the peat-forming plant communities of the European peatlands, is convinced that peat contains biostimulators and even holds out a cure for cancer), or it may just be the placebo of peaty places. Who knows for sure? However, in these enlightened days when even the multinational drug companies are paying more than lip service to the claims of ethno-medicine, it would be a foolish shareholder who would write it all off as mere mumbo-jumbo.

Peat is also finding a growing number of uses in the horticultural industry, which itself can only grow thanks to the promise of early retirement and more leisure time in the future; peat dug into the soil to improve its capacity of holding nutrients and water in a form in which they are available to plant growth; peat as a basis for soil-less composts for potting, bedding, grow-bagging . . .

Biotechnologists are now using earthworms to recycle organic waste from human and animal cultures, including ultra-intractable pig-dung. The end-product is a surfeit of worms and a rich source of nutrients; the former is fed to fish and fowl, the latter when mixed with peat is beginning to supply an enlightened and ever growing market. Waste not want not is the strategy of worm cultures. The worm

157

farm in my garden which busily works its own purpose out recycling our dustbin and garden wastes unfortunately shuts down operations in our cold Pennine winter. The prospects for worm technology in the warm wet west of Ireland are enormous, for at the same time it could clean up a number of local and national problems and add extra value to the peat before it is exported. The tankers which are now carrying raw peat to export markets in the arid east could equally well carry products with more added value at both ends of the route.

The peat-clad shores of western Ireland are also fringed with a great profusion of seaweeds, great harvests of which were in the old days collected, leached of their salt and dug in to boost the productivity of the ill-named lazybeds.

Again, modern technology is putting the backbreaking smelly promise of those seaweeds into the form of golden flakes, light as air, for export and instantly reconstituted with water into liquid feed for every corner and aspect of the garden world. As far as I can ascertain, no one has so far linked the potential of worms, waste, seaweed and peat, but I can say with my hand on my heart it will be done.

Another new development in the biotechnological field relates to a little water fern called *Azolla*. In the warmer countries of the world it is now being grown and harvested to form an organic mulch, rich in nitrogen, for living in its tissues are symbiotic micro-organisms that fix nitrogen from the atmosphere. It grows well in England but has problems when it comes to a really bad winter. In Ireland it could be grown in old peat cutaways flooded with entrophicated water; the resultant mass mixed with peat could then help to form the basis for a whole new range of say azollacomposts and that's just for starters.

Take for example the case of Erin Peat Products. They are already right in the middle of it at Birr in County Offaly. Giving employment to seventy-four people, this enlightened company works 600-plus hectares of raised bog using the most modern methods of vacuum harvesting. Its products are a range of plant pots made of peat mainly going for export. Peat is an amazingly light substance which can be given great strength by compression and still retains its insulating properties. It is thus a raw material which can be shaped to many demands.

Nature provided the Irish with a green and pleasant land and a deposit account of insulating energy which is readily available on the surface and is still in the black to the tune of at least five thousand million tonnes. At an extraction rate of five million tonnes per annum it could well last 1000 years. Whether Bord na Móna can continue exploiting it is of little importance, for hand-cutting methods could in time exploit the lot. Even the modern do-it-yourself mechanised subsurface peat 'sausage' machines could accomplish much where the big tractors could never go. These latest tractor-towed implements reach down through the living sward to extract and extrude a sausage of peat. The peat comes up from beneath the rooting layer and the machine replaces the living turf, which in theory goes on growing. These are in conservation terms a two-edged sword, for they have certainly opened up the possibility of tackling many of the less accessible bogs, yet given the hope of regeneration. There is, however, no proof that they live up to the advertisements which claim that they allow the bog to continue to grow in their natural state. There is in fact good reason to believe that after use, regeneration is poor and patchy and some species proliferate at the expense of others. They must never be used on the key four per cent which must be left in their natural state, and their use on other sites must be adequately controlled.

All the same they do offer some new ray of hope in the complex future of Irish peat for at least their manufacturers appear to have got the message that growing peatlands have a place in the landscape economy. Using these machines with care, large tracts of peatscape could be kept open and viable for wildlife, both resident and migratory, and for the benefit of the tourist industry, while at the same time giving a return to the landowner and peat products into the future. The discerning landowner or tenant may well see the advantage of not developing his or her particular part of the peat resource until the price of the product is right. Likewise, as the true value of peat *sensu stricto* rather than the value of the energy it contains is taken into consideration, it may become policy to revitalise growth in bog sites which have been cut away in the past. Such revitalisation could begin with reed bed cultivation.

Large-scale examples where successful regrowth of peat-producing plant communities can be seen in many parts of Europe. What is more, revitalisation of wetland, fen and bog development is the only economic course open for large areas of cutaway in Ireland where pumped drainage would be needed to develop it for other uses. The predominant saucer-shape of the country with a high rim and a sump in the middle must in places direct future operations in that direction. With the large machinery still on site, Bord na Móna has wonderful opportunities to turn the clocks back almost to late glacial times, recreating rivers, ponds and lakes full of fish and waterfowl, ideal for the tourists and with the promise of peat to come.

All in all, the future of the bogs of Ireland could look bright indeed. While writing this chapter I heard that the Clara Bog has been saved from development and added to the slowly growing list of reserves. Hooray, hooray! 3.86 per cent still to go! The conserved key sites would become focal points in the heritage landscape and banks of local genetic diversity, from which other areas could be restocked and rehabilitated. This all set in matrix of reed beds, conifer plantation and new broadleaved woodland, coppiced for productivity, yet home to a diversity of wildlife and wild flowers – green growing landscapes serving and being served by the population.

For anyone who is tempted to say 'It can't be done,' take care; others said that when Bord na Móna boasted that they would turn peat into electricity. Go on, lean out and switch on the light and take a careful look at the future of the resource, but do it in the firm knowledge that whatever the decision, somewhere there will be a bog taking down the evidence.

Appendix I
PLANTS AND PEAT TYPES

This list is divided according to the ten major peat types found in Europe as described by S. Tolpa (see page 26). It gives the plants which form the bulk of each peat type in order of importance. Species which play an important part in the formation of more than one type of peat are listed under each peat type. Other peat types in which the remains of a plant are found, but in the formation of which it does not play a major role, are listed in the third column.

This list has been modified to include only those plants found in Ireland. It is not, however, an exhaustive list of the peat-forming plants of Ireland. It includes only those plants which Tolpa considered to be important peat formers, in a European context.

PEAT TYPE 1

Shining pondweed	*Potamogeton lucens*	
Perfoliate pondweed	*Potamogeton perfoliatus*	
Yellow waterlily	*Nuphar lutea*	
Whorled water millfoil	*Myriophyllum verticillatum*	
Hornwort	*Ceratophyllum demersum*	
Water soldier	*Stratiotes aloides*	
White waterlily	*Nymphea alba*	2
Broad-leaved pondweed	*Potamogeton natans*	2
Ivy duckweed	*Lemna trisulca*	2
Frogbit	*Hydrocharis morsus ranae*	2, 3

PEAT TYPE 2

Bulrush	*Schoenoplectus lacustris*	1
Flote grass	*Glyceria fluitans*	
Reedmace	*Typha latifolia*	3
Lesser reedmace	*Typha angustifolia*	3
Water horsetail	*Equisetum fluviatile*	1, 3, 4
Common reed	*Phragmites australis*	1, 3, 4

PEAT TYPE 3

Common reed	*Phragmites communis*	1, 2, 4
Tufted sedge	*Carex elata*	
Acute sedge	*Carex acuta*	
Lesser pond sedge	*Carex acutiformis*	
Saw sedge	*Cladium mariscus*	
Gipsywort	*Lycopus europaeus*	
Cowbane	*Cicuta virosa*	
Panicled sedge	*Carex paniculata*	4
Greater spearwort	*Ranunculus lingua*	4
Bottle sedge	*Carex rostrata*	4, 5

PEAT TYPE 4

Small hook moss	*Drepanocladus aduncus*	3
Spear moss	*Calliergon cuspidatum*	3
Kingcup	*Caltha palustris*	
Marsh willow-herb	*Epilobium palustre*	3
Star moss	*Campylium stellatum*	3
Large hook moss	*Drepanocladus vernicosus*	
Giant spear moss	*Calliergon giganteum*	
Scorpion moss	*Scorpidium scorpioides*	
Diandrous sedge	*Carex diandra*	
Common sedge	*Carex nigra*	
Curled hook moss	*Drepanocladus revolvens*	
Carnation sedge	*Carex panicea*	
Black bog rush	*Schoenus nigricans*	
Lesser spearwort	*Ranunculus flammula*	
Marsh cinquefoil	*Potentilla palustris*	3, 5
Purple moor grass	*Molinia caerulea*	5
Sweet gale	*Myrica gale*	5
Narrow sedge	*Carex lasiocarpa*	5
White sedge	*Carex canescens*	5
Bogbean	*Menyanthes trifoliata*	5, 6
Common cotton grass	*Eriophorum angustifolium*	5, 6
Bog thread moss	*Aulacomnium palustre*	5, 7

PEAT TYPE 5

Marsh cinquefoil	*Potentilla palustris*	3, 4
Purple moor grass	*Molinia caerulea*	4
Sweet gale	*Myrica gale*	4
Narrow sedge	*Carex lasiocarpa*	4
White sedge	*Carex canescens*	4
Bogbean	*Menyanthes trifoliata*	4, 6
Common cotton grass	*Eriophorum angustifolium*	4, 6
Fine spear moss	*Calliergon stramineum*	
Floating hook moss	*Drepanocladus fluitans*	
Dark bog moss	*Sphagnum teres*	
White beak sedge	*Rhynchospora alba*	6
Mud sedge	*Carex limosa*	6
Rannoch rush	*Scheuchzeria palustris*	6
Feathery bog moss	*Sphagnum cuspidatum*	6
Recurved bog moss	*Sphagnum recurvum*	6
Cranberry	*Oxycoccus palustris*	6, 7
Bog thread moss	*Aulacomnium palustre*	4, 7

PEAT TYPE 6

Mud sedge	*Carex limosa*	5
Rannoch rush	*Scheuchzeria palustris*	5
Feathery bog moss	*Sphagnum cuspidatum*	5
Bog asphodel	*Narthecium ossifragum*	5, 7
Recurved bog moss	*Sphagnum recurvum*	5, 7
Round-leaved sundew	*Drosera rotundifolia*	5, 7

PEAT TYPE 7

Bog hair moss	*Aulacomnium palustre*	4, 5
	Polytrichum alpestre	
Polytrichum alpestre	*Polytrichum alpestre*	5
Bog cotton	*Eriophorum vaginatum*	5
Ling	*Calluna vulgaris*	5
Bog rosemary	*Andromeda polifolia*	5, 6
Papillose bog moss	*Sphagnum papillosum*	5, 6
Cross-leaved heath	*Erica tetralix*	5, 6
Bog asphodel	*Narthecium ossifragum*	5, 6
Red bog moss	*Sphagnum capillifolium*	

Burgundy red bog moss	Sphagnum magellanicum	
Brown bog moss	Sphagnum fuscum	
Crowberry	Empetrum nigrum	
Schreber's feather moss	Pleurozium schreberi	
Compact bog moss	Sphagnum compactum	

PEAT TYPE 8

Eared willow	Salix aurita	
Common sallow	Salix cinerea	
Sweet gale	Myrica gale	
Alder	Alnus glutinosa	
Marsh fern	Thelypteris palustris	
Yellow loosestrife	Lysimachia vulgaris	
Spear moss	Calligergon cuspidatum	
Woody nightshade	Solanum dulcamara	
Gipsywort	Lycopus europaeus	
Yellow flag	Iris pseudacorus	
Common reed	Phragmites communis	
Lesser pond sedge	Carex acutiformis	
Elongated sedge	Carex elongata	
Great pond sedge	Carex riparia	
Alder buckthorn	Frangula alnus	9
Squarrose bog moss	Sphagnum squarrosum	9
Blanched bog moss	Sphagnum palustre	9
Raspberry	Rubus idaeus	9
Rowan	Sorbus aucuparia	9
Fimbriate bog moss	Sphagnum fimbriatum	9
Birch	Betula pubescens	9

PEAT TYPE 9

Squarrose bog moss	Sphagnum squarrosum	8
Blanched bog moss	Sphagnum palustre	8
Raspberry	Rubus idaeus	8
Rowan	Sorbus aucuparia	8
Fimbriate bog moss	Sphagnum fimbriatum	8
Birch	Betula pubesceus	8
Wavy hair grass	Deschampsia flexuosa	
Bank hair moss	Polytrichum commune	
Wood hair moss	Polytrichum formosum	
Bilberry	Vaccinium mytillus	10
Purple moor grass	Molinia caerulea	8, 10

PEAT TYPE 10

Bilberry	Vaccinium myrtillus	9
Purple moor grass	Molinia caerulea	9
Pine	Pinus sylvestris	9
Cowberry	Vaccinium vitis idea	9
Schreber's feather moss	Pleurozium schreberi	9
Wavy spike moss	Dicranum undulatum	9
Red bog moss	Sphagnum capillaceum	9
Red feather moss	Hylocomnium splendens	9
Recurved bog moss	Sphagnum recurvum	9
Cotton grass	Eriophorum vaginatum	
Crowberry	Empetrum nigrum	
Cranberry	Oxycoccus palustris	
Ling	Calluna vulgaris	
Burgundy red bog moss	Sphagnum magellanicum	
Bog rosemary	Andromeda polifolia	

Appendix 2
LIST OF BOGS RECOMMENDED FOR CONSERVATION

RAISED BOGS (east to west)
No classic contained raised bogs are known to exist. All those listed are ridge-raised bogs.

1.   A site in County Kildare as representative of the most easterly raised bog remaining in Ireland. No undamaged site exists, but one of the following could be restored: Ballanafagh N 81 28 (130ha), Ballina N 70 42 (140ha), Monds N 78 18 (550ha).

2.   Raheenmore N 44 32 (213ha) County Offaly. One of the few State-owned raised bogs. It is drying out as a result of marginal drainage. There are no pools, but there are well-developed hummocks and hollows. The depth of peat is exceptional, being over 15m in places.

3.   Clara N 26 30 (520ha) County Offaly. One of the largest remaining midland raised bogs, containing the only well-developed examples of soak systems similar to that which occurred on Pollagh Bog. It also contains well-developed hummocks, hollows and pools. Bord na Móna attempted to drain the eastern part, but the site is now being acquired by the Forest and Wildlife Service for conservation.

4.   Mongan N 030 305 (200ha) County Offaly. Much of this bog, which is close to the monastic settlement of Clonmacnoise, is owned by An Taisce. It lies between two esker ridges and is exceptionally wet, with perhaps the best-develeloped network of pools and hummocks in the country. Parts of it have not been burnt for many years and it has a well-developed lichen flora.

5.   Lower Newtown N 01 11 (300ha) County Offaly. This bog is the only known example in Ireland possessing an extensive wet birch wood across the centre of the cupola. It is a very wet site with well-developed pools and hummocks, and is an important roosting and feeding site for the Greenland white-fronted geese which frequent the adjacent Little Brosna callows.

6. Ballyduff/Clonfinane M 00 03 (340ha) County Tipperary. This complex contains some very wet areas with well-developed pools and hummocks, a very wet flush and a small stand of pine, which is spreading across a flushed area.

7. Ballykenny N 09 79 (300ha) County Longford. The best example of a flood-plain bog and probably the most northerly intact raised bog in the country. It is very wet in places and grades into woodland and callows alongside the River Shannon. It is frequented by Greenland white-fronted geese.

8. Ardgraigue M 83 14 (175ha) County Galway. A small, very wet bog with well-developed hummocks and hollows but no pools. It contains the rare *Sphagnum pulchrum*. Recent cutting along the margins threatens the survival of this bog.

9. Lough Lurgeen M 66 59 (560ha) County Galway. A large complex bog with characteristics of blanket bogs. It has very wet areas with pools and hummocks, a lake, from which flows a small river, several flushes and at its NW end it grades into a turlough. It is a feeding and roosting site for Greenland white-fronted geese.

10. Carrowbehy M57 93 (310ha) County Roscommon. A very wet bog, more or less intact with several flushes, lakelets and well-developed pools and hummocks. It grades into fen alongside the River Suck and into incipient blanket bog on a marginal drumlin. It is very rich in plant species.

11. Addergoole M 31 34 (500ha) County Galway. A flood-plain bog and the most westerly raised bog in the country, situated on the eastern shore of Lough Corrib. It is very wet, with a small soak system. There is extensive peat-cutting around the margins, but on the NW side it appears to grade naturally into fen.

LOWLAND BLANKET BOGS (north to south)
This list includes certain sites which do not fall readily into the blanket bog category, but have certain features characteristic of raised bogs. Areas are approximate only.

1. Owenbeagh C 00 18 (17ha) County Donegal. A small bog at the head of a deep glacial valley, in the Glenveagh National Park. It forms a small dome, but has vegetation characteristic of blanket bog.

2. Lough Barra B 92 10 (1000ha) County Donegal. One of the few examples of lowland blanket bog in Donegal. It is situated in a broad valley dominated by Slieve Snaght and contains numerous pools, small lakes and rivers. It is an important site for Greenland white-fronted geese.

3. Pettigo Plateau H 04 74 (900ha) County Donegal. One of the only two peatland nature reserves in the country, this bog is situated on an undulating plateau at a higher elevation than Lough Barra Bog. There is a mixture of wet heath, bog and a complex of headwater lakes and streams. The wetter areas are frequented by Greenland white-fronted geese.

4. Easky G 42 27 and G 47 27 (970ha) County Sligo. An interesting complex at two different elevations on the northern slopes of the Ox Mountains. The areas display characteristics between lowland blanket and raised bogs and lowland and mountain bog. There are numerous pools, small lakes and rivers. Another feeding area for Greenland white-fronted geese.

5. Glenamoy F 89 35 (2000ha) County Mayo. The Irish study site of the International Biological Programme, forming part of the broad open expanse of bog in County Mayo. It is a very exposed, maritime site, containing pools, lakes, streams and flushes.

6. Owenboy G 05 16 (480ha) County Mayo. This bog lies in a broad open valley on the eastern edge of the Mayo blanket peats. It contains several domes with raised bog type vegetation, separated by broad flushes, some of which contain the rare moss *Homalothecium nitens*.

7. Owenduff F 86 07 (6000ha) County Mayo. The largest intact river catchment dominated by blanket peat remaining in the country. It forms a broad basin surrounded by the Nephin Bay Mountains and occupied by fast-flowing rivers, well-developed pool complexes and lakes. It is an area of great wilderness character and is used by Greenland white-fronted geese.

8. Connemara (20,000ha) County Galway. The area west of a line from Oughterard to Spiddal contains an extensive complex of oligotrophic lakes, poor fens, flushes, rivers and heaths within a matrix of blanket bog. Unlike in NW Mayo, the peat is broken up by frequent rock outcrops. The area is fragmented into numerous discrete units by afforestation and turf-cutting, especially in the east of the region. The area is important for several rare plants and it contains many feeding/roosting sites of the Greenland white-fronted goose. The most important areas are NW of Roundstone, N of Screeb and SE of Maam Cross.

9. Eirk V 86 76 (83ha) County Kerry. A very fine series of domes, separated by streams, occurs on the floor of the Owenreagh valley. The vegetation is characteristic of blanket bog on the domes, but it grades into fen alongside the river and streams. There are abundant pools, some being arranged concentrically on the domes.

10. Ballaghisheen V 68 80 (300ha) County Kerry. The most southerly intact area of lowland blanket bog. It is situated in a broad valley dominated by Carrauntoohill. There are very wet, pool-studded areas, streams and poor fens.

MOUNTAIN BLANKET BOG (north to south)
1. Slieve League G 55 78 (2200ha) County Donegal. Altitude 200–670m. A complex of wet heath, bog and cliffs which carry rare arctic alpine plants.

2. Ben Bulben G 73 46 (2000ha) County Sligo and County Leitrim. A limestone plateau between 400m and 500m overlain by peat. In places the limestone outcrops and scarp

of the plateau carries arctic alpine plants.

3.   Cuilcagh Plateau H 14 28 (500ha) County Cavan. A plateau between 300m and 450m covered in deep, well-developed blanket bog containing numerous pool-systems, small acid lakes and headwater streams. Erosion, due to overgrazing, is not yet a serious problem.

4.   Maumakeogh Plateau F 98 18 (2000ha) County Mayo. One of the few areas in Mayo or Galway where the terrain is flat enough for extensive mountain blanket bog to develop. It contains pool complexes, flushes and well-developed *Sphagnum* cover.

5.   Letterfrack Plateau M 03 41 (600ha) County Galway. An unusual area of bog on a lake-studded plateau at 280m with numerous flushes and pool complexes. The vegetation is transitional between lowland and mountain blanket bog and includes the rare *Sphagnum pulchrum.*

6.   Slieve Bloom Mountains N 25 10 (2230ha) County Laois and County Offaly. An extensive but narrow area of bog covers the summit ridge, which varies between 300m and 580m. It is one of the few such areas in the country not damaged by overgrazing. Its situation in the middle of the central plain is important as a link between the mountain blanket bogs of the west and those of Wicklow. The vegetation is characterised by a deep mat of *Sphagna* and lichens and includes two species characteristic of raised bogs, cranberry and bog rosemary. Most of the area is a nature reserve.

7.   Sally Gap 0 14 13 (900ha) County Wicklow. Altitude 560m. The only area of intact blanket bog remaining in the east of the country. It contains numerous pool systems and several headwater streams and the characteristic raised bog plant, bog rosemary. Being close to Dublin it is particularly valuable for educational purposes.

8.   Mangerton Mountain V 97 81 (2000ha) County Kerry. A complex of bog, wet heath and cliffs between 270m and 920m. Rare arctic alpine plants grow on the cliffs and the area is inhabited by the only native herd of red deer. Part of the area lies in the Killarney National Park.

BIBLIOGRAPHY

T.A. Barry (1969) Origins and distribution of peat types in the bogs of Ireland. *Irish Forestry* 26 (2).

Seamus Caulfield (1978) Neolithic fields — the Irish evidence. *British Archaeological Reports*, 137-43.

Seamus Caulfield (1983) The Neolithic settlement of north Connaught. *British Archaeological Reports*, 195-213.

Michael Herity (1981) A Bronze Age farmstead at Glenree in Co. Mayo. *Popular Archaeology* 2 (9) 36-7.

Frank Mitchell (1986) *The Shell Guide to Reading the Irish Landscape.* Country House, Dublin.

John J. Moore (1955) The distribution and ecology of *Scheuchzeria palustris* on a raised bog in Co. Offaly. *The Irish Naturalist's Journal* 11 (12).

John J. Moore (1968) *A classification of the Bogs and Wetlands of Northern Europe.* Vereinigung für Vegetationskunde, Stolzenau/Weser.

Robert Lloyd Praeger (1909) *A Tourist's Flora of South West Ireland.* Hodges & Figgis, Dublin.

Robert Lloyd Praeger (1937) *The Way That I Went.* Allen Figgis, Dublin.

Robert Lloyd Praeger (1941) *A Populous Solitude.* Methuen, London.

J.B. Ryan and John Cross (1984) The conservation of peatlands in Ireland. *Proc. 7th International Peat Congress* 1, 388-405.

H. Van Eck, A. Govers, A. Lemaire and J. Shaminee (1984) *Irish Bogs A Case For Planning.* Catholic University of Nijmegen.

INDEX

Plants are indexed under their English names unless there is no generally accepted English equivalent. See Appendix 1 for Latin names of peat-forming plants. References to plates or captions are in *italic script*.

Achill Island, County Mayo 73
acidification 27, 37
    by bog mosses 28, 30
acidity 24-5, 58-9, 82-3
    affected by rainfall 84
    caused by wet climate 59
    and flora 86
acid rain 37, 86
Addergoole Bog 164
aerenchyma 18, 19
aerobic life 17-19
afforestation of peatland 132, 152-5
agriculture 41
    development of bogs for 37, 38, 151-2
    genetic information for 85-6
    modern 109
    pre-bog 995, 109-18, 148
        in the stone ages 14, 92-3, 123
        in bronze age 112, 123-5
        in iron age 25
        in early Christian period 126
        in Anglo-Norman and Tudor times 127-8
    speeds peat initiation 110
alder 37, 85, 90, 91
    decline and increases 92, 123-8
algae 44, 45, 73
aluminium 84
Amara alpina 90
anaerobic zone 19-20, 22, 27
Anglo-Normans 127
archaeology 90, 95
    artefacts 126
    finds at Belderg 110-11
    Lagore 125-6
arctic-alpine plants 76, 89, 90, 165, 166

Ardgraigue Bog 164
ash 90
    appears, declines and increases 123-8
    penalty for felling 126
Azolla 156

Balla, County Mayo 119
Ballaghisheen Bog 165
Ballanafagh Bog 163
Ballina Bog 163
Ballyduff/Clonfinane Bog 164
Ballykenny Bog 164
Ballyscullion Bog 54
bearberry 58, 76
bedrock 57-8
beech 122
beetles 90
Behy/Glenulra, County Mayo 95, 109
Belcoo 75
Bellacorick, County Mayo 154
bell heather 73
Ben Bulben 58, 165
bicarbonate 24, 27, 81-5
bilberry 37, 77
biotechnology 156-8
birch 37, 45, 48, 89, 90
    increases and declines 92, 123-7
birds, in mesolithic diet 90-1
Bishopsland period 114, 123, 124
bittersweet 128
black bog rush 16, 27, 73, 76-7, 84, *13, 33*
Blackwater complex 41
bladderwort 12, 20, 21, *7*
Bloomhill, County Offaly 115, 118

blue moor grass 79
bog
    adaptations to life on the 20-5
    bodies 119-20
    butter 118-19, 127
    chemistry 81-5, 80-6
    as store of energy and information 12, 17
        23-4, 86, 87-128
    definitions of 26, 30, 38
    development and growth of 29-30, 37-8, 42-3,
        58-9, 93-3, 109-10
        instigated and speeded by farming 111, 114
        in lake basin 53, 54, 57
        stages listed 29-30
    development (exploitation) of 130-2, 145-60
    'floating' 53-4
    flora 14, 42, 79-83, 84
        acidity, rainfall and 86
        blanket 73-7, 85
        raised 84
    hoards 113-14, 123
    indicator of environmental change 86
    (or peat) profiles 42, 43
    pH 75
    pools 44, 74, 75
    as a resource 129-60
    surface dries out 37, 42
    toghers 115, 118
    wood 119
bog asphodel 12, 22, 28, 79, 13, 16
    ecologically similar to Rannoch rush 49
bogbean 27, 28, 13
bog bursts 50-4, 57
bog cotton 12, 22, 27
    many-flowered 28, 79
    single-flowered 28, 45
    broad-leaved cotton-grass 75
bog lousewort 73
bog moss 30
    see also Sphagnum
Bog of Allen 11, 26, 37, 41, 48, 55, 91
bog pimpernel 23-4
bog pondweed 74
bog rosemary 73, 166
bog types
    blanket 38, 39, 55, 56-60, 73-7, 83, 13
        lowland 38, 82
        mountain 38, 85
    comparison of 73-4, 77
    intermediate 83

red or raised 38, 39-55, 57
    contained 54
    flood-plain 54
    ridge-raised 54, 55, 82
    see also peat types
booleying 127, 128
Boora Bog 11
Bord na Móna 14, 29, 37, 59
    and conservation 131, 132, 145, 150, 159
    development of bogs 130-1, 150, 155
    research 151, 153, 155
    third development programme 130, 131
Borth Bog, Wales 51
Boyne valley 92
bracken 123, 125, 127
Breutelia chrysocoma 58
broad-leaved plantain 92
Broighter hoard 113
bronze age
    agriculture 124
    hoards 113-14, 125
    people 110-11, 112
    technology 111, 112, 113
Brosna, River 26, 39, 45
Bryum pseudotriquetrum 48
buckler fern
    broad 48
    narrow 46
bulbous bush 75
bulrush 27, 75
Burren 58
butterwort 20, 19
    pale 73, 79, 18

C^{14} 121, 122
calcium 22, 24, 81, 82, 83
    needed by giant deer 87
callow 26, 41
Camplyopus atrovirens 74, 79, 83
capillary action 39, 43
carbon dioxide 23
carnivorous plants 20-2
Carrauntoohil 165
Carrowbehy Bog 164
Castleblaney, County Galway 120
cattle
    cows confiscated as penalty for tree-felling 126
    modern 111
    pass mugwort seeds 127
    pre-bog farmers' 93, 114, 127

Caulfield, Seamus
    and Belderg Beg 110
    description of Behy 95, 109
central plain 11, 37, 41, 92
    site for raised bogs 39
cereal 110, 111, 114
    mills 118
    increases and declines 124-5, 127
chalk 93
Chartley Moss, England 53-4
chemistry of bog waters 81-5
chert 91
chestnut 154
chloride 81, 82, 83
chlorophyll 22, 24
Christianity 16, 126, 148, 149
Cladopodiella fluitans 44
Clara Bog 48, 159, 163
climate
    affects growth of domes 39
    changes in, reflected in peat layers 50
    changes in, in geological time 88-91
    climatic optimum 91
    of Ireland, warm, wet, and oceanic 38, 58
    in neolithic period 93, 109, 123
    pre-neolithic 110
    Poulter Index 130
    speeds peat-growth 112
Clonmacnoise, County Offaly 163
Clonsast, County Offaly 153
cloudberry 77, *27*
Coalman 145
coloration changes 44
Connemara 59, 60, 165
conservation
    of bogs 16, 131-2, 146-50, 159
    of water by plants on bogs 23-4
copper 110, 113, 123
coppicing 153-6, *57*
cores of peat 29
Corlona Bog 118
Cornish heath 75-6
corn spurrey 111
cottage industry 155
cotton-grass *28*
    broad-leaved 75
cranberry 12, 23-4, 28, 166, *21*
    rare on blanket bog 73, 77
crannogs 115, 124
    Lagore crannog 125

crops
    cereal at Belderg 110, 111
    modern 111
    neolithic farmers' 92-3
    in Tudor times 128
Cross, Eric 145
cross-leaved heath 12, 79
crowberry 90
Cuilcagh Plateau 166
cultivation ridges 111
cupola, *see* domes
curlew 12, *1*
Curragh, County Kildare 15
cyclops *5*

daisies 124, 128
damsel fly 12, *6*
dandelion 124
Darwin, Charles 20
decomposer organisms 18, 19, 85
decomposition 19, 22, 85
Denmark 120
dentrification 85
Department of Fisheries and Forestry 155
Derrandoran Bog 51
Derrycooly 48
Derrynaflan hoard 113, *45, 46*
Diacheila arctica 90
dock 89, 92, 123
domes
    development and growth of 30, 39-43, 91
    like a drop of water 44
    height 39, 45
    tension on 44
    water table in 30, 39, 43
Dorset heath 75
Dowris period 114, 124
dragonfly 20
drainage 28, 37
    of callows 41
    caused by turf-cutting 53, 153
    causing flooding 49
    depressions 45
    endangering bogs 132
    for forestry 153
    prevents formation of blanket bog 57
Drumkeragh, County Down 119
duck, in mesolithic diet 91

earthworms 157-8
Easky Bog 165
Edinburgh Botanic Garden 75
Eirk Bog 165
electricity 11, 14
    from turf 129, 130-1, 159-60, *55*
    from wood 154
elm 90, 91, 154
    decline 92, 123
    increases and declines with agriculture 124-8
    penalty for felling 126
emperor moth *22*
energy 18
    from fossil fuels 154
    renewable sources of 154, 156-7
    see also turf: as fuel
Ennerdale Water, England 80
Eogan, George 113
erica 58
Erin Peat Products 158
erosion 57, 73
Erris 59-60
evaporation 23, 39,
    uncommon in Irish climate 58, 82
evapotranspiration 39, 92

Fairy Water Bog 50, 53
Fallahogy Bog 54
fen 26, 30, 37, 57, 84, 91
    fed by flowing groundwater 59, 75
    flora 46, 47, 75, 89
      similar to blanket bogs 74-5, 79-83, 84
    in neolithic times 92-3
    nitrogen fixers on 95
    pH 75
    spring-fed 46
    see also poor fen
fen peat *see* peat types
fertiliser 21, 23, 86
fish, in mesolithic diet 91
fish farming 157
flint 90, 91
    slug knife 111
floating mat 27, 28, 30
flooding of Pollagh 48
flooding horizon 43

forest 90-3, 110, *37*
    cover in Ireland 152
    cycles of decline and recovery 124-8
    fen 91, 92-3
      forestry on 151, 152-6; drainage for 153
    replaced by grassland 109
    secondary 92
    see also afforestation
Forest and Wildlife Service 132, 146, 150, 163
fox 89
fraughan *see* bilberry
frog 13, *38*
frogbit 27
fulachta fiadh 114-15
funnel-shaped depression 46-8
furze *17*

Garry Bog 51, 53
Gearagh, The, County Cork 132, 145-6
German bogs, chemistry of 81, 82
giant deer 87-90
Gibbins 145
gipsywort 27
Glenamoy Bog 165
Glenveagh National Park 164
goose 22
    Greenland white-fronted 13, 22, 46, 163-5, *56*
goosefoot 124, 126, 127
Gowlan River 41
Grand Canal 45
grasses 73, 89, 93
    increase and decline with agriculture 124-5, 127
grassland, replaces forest 109, 123, 128
graves, neolithic 92, 95
Great Divide 59
Grenzhorizont 50, 124
groundwater, flowing
    bog growing above level of 28, 30, 39
    enrichment of, by leaching 59
    flushing agent 27
    impeded by plant growth 30
    influences mineral-rich peatlands 37, 59, 81, 82
    paludification and 41
    sources of nutrients 27, 28
grouse 22, *36*
Grundlenried, Germany 47

hare 22, 89, *8*
hazel 90, 91, 154
    increase and declines 92, 123-8
    nuts in mesolithic diet 91
    penalty for felling 126
heather 23, 28, 76, *17, 25*
    pollen at Lagore 125-6
    see also individual plant names
heath milkwort 73
hen harrier *40*
Herity, Michael 111
Hickey, Timothy 145-6
Hill of Usnagh 26
history and prehistory, stored in bogs 25, 87-128, 129, *41*
hollows *see* hummocks and
Homalothecium nitens 76, 165
horizontal mills 118
hornbeam 154
horticulture, peat in 157, 158
hummocks 12, *3, 14*
  growth of 42
  and hollows 42, 60
  and pools 73
  mosses that form 42, 51
  surface dries out 28, 42
  hydrogen ions 24

ice ages 88-90
International Peat Society 130
ionic tables 81-3
Irish heath 75
Irish Peatlands Conservation Council 132
Irish Wildlife Federation 132
iron 12, 125, 126
    pan 59

Jessen, Knud 114
Juncus kochii 46
juniper 89, 90
  dwarf 76

Keenagh, County Longford 118
kermi 45

kidney saxifrage 76
Kilkee 83
Killarney, County Kerry 14, 155, 166
Knockboy, County Galway 152

lagg 41
Lagore crannog 125, 126
lakes 26, 47
    starting point for raised bog 39, *10, 12*
land, depressions of, in ice ages 88
Larnian people 91
lawns 42
leaching 58, 59, 82, 84
    after ice age 89, 91
    neolithic farming opens soil to 92, 93
    increases in bronze age 124, 125
lemming 89
Letterfrack Plateau 166
lichens 12, 28, 42, 43, 50, 163
lime 24
lime (tree) 154
limestone, blanket bog forms on 58
ling 12, 23, 28, 42, 45, 58, *25*
Little Brosna River 48, 163
Little Island, County Cork 118
liverwort 44, 74
loess 80
Lough Barra Bog 164
Lough Boora 91
Lough Lurgeen 164
Lower Newtown Bog 48, 163
lusitanian flora 75-6, 79

Mackay's heath 75
Macroom, County Cork 132, 145
magnesium 24, 81, 82, 83
Mangerton Mountain 166
marl 46
marsh cinquefoil 27, 48
marsh gas or methane 19
marsh pennywort 48, 75
Maumakeogh Plateau 166
Meesia triquetra 76
mesolithic people 90-1
microliths 90

migration 88-90
millfoil 27
mineral deficiency on bogs 20, 24, 58
    strategies for coping with 20-5
mineral enrichment
    indications of 45-6, 48
mineral-rich peatlands 37
mineral soil 20
    blanket bog forms on 57
minerals and nutrients 12, 17, 20
    in bog water 81-5
    in fen water 82
    in groundwater 27, 29, 59
    held in cycle 22-3, 58, 85-6
    leached out of soil 58, 93
    loss of 22-3
    in rainwater 80, 83, 84
    recycling of 22-3, 28, 85
    released from breakdown of peat 45
    removed from soil by neolithic farming 92,93
    from sea-spray 80, 83
Mitchell, Frank 57, 121, 122
monasteries 113
monastic way of life 125, 126
Monds Bog 163
Mongan Bog 163
Monmor Bog 83
Moore, Fr John J. 13, 28, 47-9
mor 91
mosses
    bank hair 28, 42
    Breutelia chrysocoma 58
    brown 27, 30, 75
    Bryum pseudotriquetrum 48
    feather 27
    feathery bog 12
    fork 28, 42
        white 28, 42
    Homalothecium nitens 76
    hummock-forming 51
    lambswool 12, 28, 9
    Meesia triquetra 76, 165
    scorpion 27, 75, 80
    spear 27
    star 27
    see also Sphagnum mosses
mountain avens 76, 90
mountain sorrel 90

Mount Dillon Bord na Móna works 156-7
mugwort 89, 124, 127

nettle 92
neolithic
    implements and pottery 110
    people 91-3, 123
Nephin Bay Mountains 165
Newgrange 92
Ninth International Plant Geographic Excursion 145
nitrogen 21, 84
    nitrates 73, 85, 86
    fixing 73, 85
nutrients see minerals

oak 90, 91, 110, 154
    declines and recovers 92, 123-8
    penalty for felling 126
oceanic plants 49, 79
Ó Laoghaire, An tAthair Peadar 145
Ó Riada, Seán 145
osmosis 21
Owenbeagh Bog 164
Owenboy Bog 165
Owenduff Bog 165
oxidation, corrosive 44
Ox Mountains 165
oxygen
    in water 18, 26-7
    necessary for life 17-19

Pale, the 127
paludification 41
peat
    conditions for growth 17
    cover of Ireland 38, 41
    definition of 17
    formation of 26-30, 91, 93, 109-110
    growth of 39-41
        climate and 112
        other actors and 112
        speeded up 4000 years ago 112
    layers in 29, 49-50, 54, 58
        become separated 50, 53
    precursor 50
    regeneration of 159
    stages in development, listed 29

peat-forming plants 25-6, 42
peatlands 26
  see also bog, fen, poor fen
peat types 25-6, 29, 37
  bog forest peats, true 37, 41, 77
  fen forest peats 37
  fen peats 30, 39, 41, 46, 50, 81
    precede development of raised bog 57
    do not precede development of blanket bog 77
  forest peats 37
  poor fen peats 83
  poor fen forest peats 37
  Tolpa's, listed 26
    lake and pond weed peats 26, 29, 30, 81
    reed peats 26, 29
    large sedge peats 26, 29
    brown moss and small sedge peats 26, 29
    mineral bog moss peats 26, 29
    aquatic bog moss peats 26, 29, 30
    true bog moss peats 26, 29, 30, 37, 39, 50, 81
    alder wood peats 26
    birch wood peats 26
    pine wood peats 26
perennials 27, 30
Pettigo Plateau 164
pH
  affects aluminium 84
  of bogs, fens, etc 81-3
  of rain, dropping 86
  scale 25
  and sweet gale 85
Philipstown 11
phosphine 19
phosphorous 21
photosynthesis 18, 19, 23, 24
  light and 44
phytoplankton 18, 36
pig, in mesolithic diet 91
pine 37, 90, 91, 93, 164
  declines in neolithic period 123
  extinct by AD 300
  as forestry crop 154
  stumps 110, *43*
pipewort 74, 76, 79, 83, *30*
pitcher plant 20, *4*
plantain 124
Pleurozia purpurea 74, 79, *26*

plough 111
  ard 125
  coulter 125
  mouldboard 126-7
podsol 59, 93
Pollagh Bog 37, 39, 41, 45, 163
  flooding of 48, 49, 53
  formation of 26-30
  home of Rannoch rush 46
  soak 45, 47
pollarding 153, 154
pollen 111, 112
  analysis 88-93, 121-8
  diagram *23*
pond horsetail 27
pondweed 27
pond weeds 26
pools *see* bog: pools *and* hummocks: and pools
poor fen 30, 37, 57
  development of 92
  nitrogen fixers on 85
potassium 21, 24, 81, 82, 84
potato 128
  blight 149
Poulter Index 129-30, 132, 153
Praeger, Robert Lloyd 11, 51, 113, 145, 146
  description of bog burst 51-4
  description of Connemara 60
  description of Erris 59-60
  description of Scragh Bog 54
precipitation 39
purple loosestrife 48
purple marsh saxifrage 90
purple moor grass 46, 48, 73, 79, 80, 83, *13*, *33*, *34*

quartzite 93

radiocarbon dating 122
Raheenmore 163
rain
  and bog growth 57-8
  slightly acid 58
  as source of nutrients 28, 30, 80, 84
rainfall 39, 80, 84, *32*
  and flora 86

rain forests, tropical 23
Raleigh, Sir Walter 128
Rannoch Moor, Perthshire 28
Rannoch rush 28, 45, *20*
    story of 46-9
Rapemills River 48
raths 124, 125
recycling of minerals and nutrients 85
    disrupted by neolithic farming 109
Red Bog 54, 112, 121-8
red deer 91, 166
reed 14, *52*
    common 14, 27, 29, 74
    as possible bog crop 156-7, 159
reedmace 27, *53*
regeneration complex 42, 45, 60
reindeer 89
relict populations of plants 90
reservoirs, compensating hidden 50-4
restructuring of soil in ice age 89
rhizomes 22
rhododendron 155
rickets 22
ring-barking 92, 123
Roundstone, County Galway 75
royal fern 48
rush 23, 27, 93
    see also names of individual rushes

St Dabaeoc's heath 75
Sally Gap Bog 166
salmon 26
Saxons 128
Scandinavia 44, 156
Scragh Bog 54
scraw 27
sea level, changes in ice ages 88
sedge 23, 27, 30, 37, 73, 89, 93, *13*
    acute 27
    bottle 27, 46, 48
    brown-beaked 79
    carnation 79
    common 46
    deer 28, 79
    mud 47
    panicled 27

saw 27, 47-8, 74, 93
slender 27
star 48
tawny 75
white-beaked 93
yellow-beaked 27, 47
Shannon estuary 11
Shannon, River 26, 41, 164
sheep 22, 132
siochs 11
sitka spruce 153
Slieve Bloom Mountains 166
Slieve League 165
Slieve Snaght 164
slope and blanket bog 57, 59
slug knife, bronze age 111
smooth rush 48
snipe 12, 46, *39*
soak 29, 45-6, 48, *11*
    pH of 75
sodium 24, 80, 81, 82, 83
soil
    restructured by ice age 89
    waterlogged 18
    woodland, affected by neolithic farming 93
sorrel 89
souterrains 125
spearwort
    greater 27
    lesser 75
Sperrin Mountains 77
Sphagnum mosses 83, *3*
    acidify environment 25
    less abundant on blanket bog 73
    structure of 23-4
    S. capillifolium 28, 42, 43, 44
    S. cuspidatum 28, 42, 43, 45
      in Achill 73
      indicates wettest places in bogs 93
      in Pollagh soak 46-8
      peat 50
      typical of bog pools 49
    S. fuscum 28, 42, 43
    S. imbricatum 28, 37, 42, 43, *16*
      hummocks formed of 51
      peat 50
    S. magellanicum 28, 37, 42, 43, 44

S. palustre 37, 43, 44
S. papillosum 28, 42, 43
S. pulchrum 42, 166
S. recurvum 28
S. squarrosum 37
S. subnitens 43
S. subsecundum 28, 43, 79
S. tenellum 42, 43
S. teres 27
spike rush
  common 75
  many-stemmed 73, 80
spring gentian 76, 90
standstill horizon 43
stomata 23
stone ages 90-3
stone implements 92, 123
strawberry tree 76
subfossils 25, 87
sulphate 19, 81, 82
sulphide 19
sulphuric acid 19
sundew 12, 20, *13*
  great 28
  long-leaved 20, 28, 93
  round-leaved 28
survey
  of Irish peat cover (1809-14), 38
  of raised bog flora (1958) 42-3
sweet gale 73, 79, 80, 83, *29*
  and nitrogen fixers 85
  key pH for 85
sweet vernal grass 46, 48

An Taisce 132, 163
third development programme, Bord na Móna's
  130, 131
thistles 124
Thorne Waste, England 51
timber 128, 156
  as fuel 154, 156
tobacco 128
toghers 115, 118
Toler, Tommy 111, 112
Tolpa, Stanislaus 25, 29
  peat-types identified by 26, 29, 30

tormentil 73
tourism 148-50, 157, 159
trackways, log 112-18
Trinity College radiocarbon laboratory 122
trout 27
Tudors 128
tufas 46
Tullamore 11, 13
turf
  as fuel 111, 131, 152-6
    for electricity 130-1
    non-polluting 50, 86, 131
  bogs developed to produce 130-1, 155-67
  see also peat
turf-cutting 15, 29, 37, 41, 48, 112, 132, *50, 54*
  with 'sausage' machines 158-9
Turf Development Act (1981) 132
Twelve Bens 57, 93

Valencia Island, County Kerry 115
venison
  cooked in fulachta fiadh 114-15
  rare in neolithic diet 93
Vikings 113, 127

water 17
  chemistry of bogs 27, 81-5
  conservation of, by plants 23-4
water flea 21, *5*
waterlily 27
  white 74
water lobelia 74, 76, 83
water shrimp 21
water stress 23, 50
  strategies for coping with 23-4
water table 42
  moves upwards as bog grows 43
  see also domes
water violet *31*
watery conditions, life in 17-19
Watts, Bill 121
will-o'-the-wisp 19
willow 37, 48, 89, 90, 154
Wynbunbury Moss, England 49

xeromorphic plants 23-5

yellow marsh saxifrage 76, 90
yellow mountain saxifrage 76, 90
yew 90

Zygogonium ericotorum 44